FLOWERS IN COLOR

FLOWERS IN COLOR

Sixty plates in ten colours
after the originals by Hans Schwarzenbach
Text by Professor W. Rytz
Translated and adapted by
Herbert L. Edlin

A STUDIO BOOK
THE VIKING PRESS
NEW YORK

Published 1960 by The Viking Press, Inc.
625 Madison Avenue, New York 22, New York

Translated from 'Notre Belle Flore'
published by Editions du Message, Berne
Color plates printed in Switzerland
Text printed in the Netherlands

Introduction

EVERY lover of flowers longs to preserve the fleeting beauty of his cherished blossoms after they have faded, and to anticipate their charms in the dead season of the year before spring re-awakens each plant to life. Here the skill of the gifted artist Hans Schwarzenbach holds in the full glory of their natural colours those blooms that we most admire in garden or wilderness, by streamside or on hill. His choice includes many of the jewels of the Alps that now enrich English and American rock gardens, and his discerning eye has brought in familiar plants of the flower beds such as daffodil and sunflower, and even the humble dandelion — a weed to the gardener but a joy to any painter.

What a delight it is to turn page after page and find flowers chosen by an artist for grace of form and intensity of colour, rather than those picked out by a gardener just because they are easy to grow, or by a botanist because of their rarity! Yet this rich medley of shapely outlines and glowing hues is linked to our everyday experience, for flowers like these — if not always of precisely the same species — grace our meadows, woods, and borders every spring and summer.

Allied to the artist's brush and pen, the skill of the lithographic printer has recorded each plant's true likeness, and nearly always in its natural size. Eyes keener than a camera's lens, hands more sensitive than a photographic plate, have here reproduced the essence of every chosen flower, so faithfully that you feel you can almost pluck it from the page. Thus the brilliant study of the scarlet corn poppy gives the lie to Burns's famous lines:

But pleasures are like poppies spread:
You seize the flower, its bloom is shed.

Further, each plate is in itself a work of art, with colours in contrast or harmony to intrigue or to satisfy the discerning onlooker. Always the plants shown on any page are members of the same botanical family, so that there is some underlying kindred resemblance to unite their individual patterns and shades.

The text, based on the work of the distinguished Swiss botanist Professor W. Rytz of the Berne Botanical Institute, links the plants with our human life and experience. Many of those selected have long been raised, on both sides of the Atlantic, as herbs, and some still have a place in the medicine chest. Strange fragments of folk lore or associations with religion have become attached to certain flowers, and have been handed down by those who have tended them, from one generation to the next, wherever they may have settled. Here we are told the origins of odd plant names like 'Touch-me-not' and 'Ragged Robin', or may learn which herb is best for poisoning wolves!

Many flowers owe their peculiar structure to some remarkable process essential to secure their cross-fertilization; this is lucidly explained in a fascinating way. Details are given of each plant's home in the wilds, whether in marsh, in meadow, or on mountain. Such knowledge will aid both the gardener who raises the cultivated strains and the roving botanist who delights to discover the wild plant in its natural surroundings.

The text holds many facts hitherto unknown or unappreciated by flower-lovers. It will help every reader to enjoy the outstanding colour plates and to appreciate the flowers themselves as each unfolds in its due season.

H. L. Edlin

FLOWERS IN COLOR

PLATE 1

Daffodil Family *Amaryllidaceae*

Pheasant's Eye Narcissus

Narcisse des poètes
Narcissus poeticus

Daffodil

Narcisse
Narcissus pseudonarcissus

Snowdrop

Perce-neige
Galanthus nivalis

Spring Snowflake

Niveole de printemps
Leucojum vernum

1

Pheasant's Eye Narcissus

Narcisse des poètes *Narcissus poeticus*

To see this flower in the full splendour of its natural home, you must go to the Alps or the Jura, in April and May; there you will wonder whether the white carpet that stretches before you into the distance is snow or narcissus. But in England and America it is mainly a garden flower, though sometimes you will find it naturalised, by accident or design, in the woods.

The snow-white beauty of the flower is enhanced by the inner cup, shaped like a golden bowl with a crinkly margin fired with orange-red. It is this cup that gives rise to the name of 'pheasant's eye'. The pheasant's eye is the principal ancestor of most of the short-cupped narcissi grown for garden display and indoor decoration.

2

Daffodil

Narcisse *Narcissus poeticus*

In this species the cup is developed into a long tube with an open mouth, of a fine golden yellow shade; while the corolla, in the strict sense, consists of six large pale yellow petals.

In England the wild daffodil is a woodland plant, but local in its spread. There are famous drifts around Eastnor Castle in Herefordshire, at Farndale in East Yorkshire, and at Dunnerdale in the Lake District. In the Alps, however, it flourishes amid the pastures, often blooming on the edge of snowfields, just after the crocuses.

The Greek name of *Narcissus* refers to the drowsy feeling caused by the smell of massed flowers, although any single blossom alone has a delightful scent. In Wales, where it ranks as a national emblem, the daffodil is called *cenhinen Bedr* — St Peter's leek.

This wild daffodil is the parent stock of nearly all the long-trumpeted narcissi that make so brave a show each spring in American and European gardens.

3

Snowdrop

Perce-neige *Galanthus nivalis*

The natural range of the wild snowdrop, which is truly native in Britain, extends across southern Europe, and it has also been introduced to North American gardens. In Wales it is called *eirlys* — herb of the snow, or else *cloch maban* — the baby's bell.

The snowdrop blooms from January to March, usually in leafy groups amid woodlands. Each underground bulb sends up only two narrow leaves and one stem bearing a solitary flower. Each graceful drooping blossom has three narrow outer petals that are pure white, and three inner petals that are white with green tips, making a charming composition.

4

Spring Snowflake

Niveole de printemps *Leucojum vernum*

Rare in Britain, the spring snowflake grows sparingly in copses and along hedgerows in Dorset; it is commoner in Europe, and is raised as a garden plant in North America. More robust than the snowdrop, it produces stouter leaves; the flower is larger and more open, and has six white petals of equal length, each flecked with green at the tip.

1
2
3
4
Hans Schwarzenbach 53

PLATE 2

Periwinkle Family *Apocynaceae*

Lesser Periwinkle

Petite Pervenche
Vinca minor

Greater Periwinkle

Grande Pervenche
Vinca major

1

Lesser Periwinkle

Petite Pervenche — *Vinca minor*

There are many places where this pretty plant is found as an escape from cultivation, and it grows as a wildling, more often than not, close to dwellings. However, it is accounted a true native of Britain, as well as of Europe, where it may be met with far from any garden. In America, it is raised as a garden plant, occasionally naturalised in shrubberies and woodlands.

The lesser periwinkle spreads widely by means of its long layer shoots, over the surface of the ground, sending up here and there its tufts of flowers. These flowers are usually blue, but varieties are found with deep mauve or dark violet blossoms; white flowers are very rare. Self-fertilisation is impossible, since a ring bearing hairs bars the entrance to the tube of the corolla, wherein the stamens are placed. Butterflies and long-tongued bees are the only insects which can effect fertilisation, but even so seed-bearing is infrequent.

2

Greater Periwinkle

Grande Pervenche — *Vinca major*

The greater periwinkle grows wild in the French Midi, and elsewhere in southern Europe, but has become naturalised in Britain and in America. It may be found in shrubberies and woodlands as an escape from the flower bed. As the name suggests, it is larger and more robust than the foregoing kind. Its flowers, which are up to two inches across, have a curious twist to the left when in bud. The petals are cut off in a peculiar oblique fashion, and the tube of the corolla opens in a remarkable five-sided mouth. The name periwinkle, with its suggestion of circular movement, is remarkably apt for this twisted, though attractive, flower; but it is actually drawn from the Latin verb *vincio*, to bind, from the use of the cord-like stems for tying bundles.

1
2
Hans Schwarzenbach 51.

PLATE 3

Balsam Family *Balsaminaceae*

Touch-Me-Not

Ne me touchez pas
Impatiens noli-tangere

Touch-Me-Not

Ne me touchez pas *Impatiens noli-tangere*

Seldom do we find a plant called by a simple catch-phrase. But the name of this one — whether in English, French, or Latin — arises in a striking fashion from a well-established idiom. The 'touch-me-not' refers only to the ripe fruit, a long, green, and fragile pod. At the slightest touch, the five side walls break away and roll themselves up from the base to the tip, scattering the seeds explosively. The same character gives rise to the Latin name for the genus, *Impatiens*. This species is also known as yellow balsam.

The flower likewise shows some peculiar features. Both the calyx and the corolla are golden yellow in colour; the trumpet-shaped spur, which has a swollen mouth and ends in a tip that is bent back in the shape of a hook, is actually a modified sepal. The corolla is shaped like a pair of jaws, and bears red spots on its inner surface.

The touch-me-not grows most frequently in groups in places having a fresh soil, yet moist and shaded, for example, along streamsides; on the whole it is a rare plant. Rather more common is the small yellow balsam, *Impatiens parviflora*, which was introduced from Siberia and Mongolia, and has a straight spur to its flower. Commoner still is the showy Indian balsam, *I. glandulifera*, which has pinkish-purple flowers and grows profusely along river banks, especially in industrial districts. This, too, is an alien plant, but handsome enought to be appreciated by many English and American gardeners.

Hans Schwarzenbach 48.

PLATE 4

Borage Family *Boraginaceae*

Water Forget-Me-Not

Myosotis des marais
Myosotis scorpioides

Mountain Lungwort

Pulmonaire des montagnes
Pulmonaria montana

Common Lungwort

Pulmonaire officinale
Pulmonaria officinalis

1

Water Forget-Me-Not

Myosotis de marais *Myosotis scorpioides*

This dainty plant can be found in ditches, marshes, and damp fields over the greater part of Europe, Asia, and America. The French often call it *Ne me oubliez pas*, and it has similar names signifying 'Forget-me-not' in other European tongues. One legend even tells of a love-sick swain who leaned too far over a river to gather a bunch for his maiden, and exclaimed 'Forget-me-not' as he was swept away, leaving the flowers as a keepsake.

This typical member of the borage family is easily recognised by its bristly leaves, which are rounded off towards the tip. These two features recall a mouse's ear, and are the origin of the plant's Latin name (derived from the Greek) literally 'mouse-ear'. The flowers are at first rose-pink, owing to the presence of acid sap, but soon become a beautiful cobalt blue as the sap becomes alkaline. The tube of the corolla is very short and ends in a ring of scales, normally yellow but occasionally pink or white, which line its throat.

2

Mountain Lungwort

Pulmonaires des montagnes *Pulmonaria montana*

This handsome plant, native to the moist woods and thickets of Central Europe, is occasionally found in gardens, though it has not established itself in the woods of Britain or America. It is a sturdy plant, with stouter stems and larger leaves and flowers than those of the common lungwort. Its flower-heads are rich in glandular hairs, while its leaves feel silky rather than bristly, and lack spots.

It appears that all the lungworts owe their use in herbal medicine to a confusion of ideas. The spotted leaves of the common kind suggested the appearance of the human lung; hence infusions of these leaves were prescribed to cure chest troubles. Both the English and the Latin names are derived from this belief.

3

Common Lungwort

Pulmonaire officinale *Pulmonaria officinalis*

In garden plots, and in those woods and hedgerows where it has become naturalised, this European plant blooms freely in earliest spring. Like the wood anemone, the celandine, the primrose and the wild arum, it comes into leaf very early so that it can use the light that penetrates through the still leafless trees above. Its leaves are marked by curious pale blotches, the purpose of which is unknown. One legend declares that they arose from drops of milk shed by the Virgin Mary, and this belief gives rise to the plant's curious folk name, 'Joseph and Mary'.

The flowers of the common lungwort, like those of many other plants of the borage family, are at first red, but soon become blue; flowers of both colours are seen together on one stem.

Like the primroses, the lungworts bear two kinds of flowers, some with a long style and short stamens, others with a short style and long stamens. This difference encourages cross-fertilisation.

1
2
3
Hans Schwarzenbach 51.

PLATE 5

Bellflower Family *Campanulaceae*

Nettle-Leaved Bellflower

Campanule gantelée
Campanula trachelium

Harebell

Campanule à feuilles rondes
Campanula rotundifolia

Bearded Bellflower

Campanule barbue
Campanula barbata

1

Nettle-Leaved Bellflower

Campanule gantelée *Campanula trachelium*

The bellflowers or campanulas are delightful flowers that well merit the place they have secured in our gardens. This particular kind is found in most of Europe, North Africa, and Siberia. In Britain it is common on the chalk downs of the south, but scarce elsewhere, though it grows sparingly in the Scottish Lowlands and south-east Ireland. It springs up in thickets and hedgerows, woodland verges and clearings, where it reaches a height of three feet, and so catches the eye. It bears large and handsome flowers, from one to one-and-a-half inches long; these may be known by their bristly haired lobes. The leaves are like those of the nettle, but do not sting. Sometimes one finds white-flowered specimens, both in gardens and in the wilds.

2

Harebell

Campanule à feuilles rondes *Campanula rotundifolia*

Although the name of this charming campanula is conventionally spent 'harebell', suggesting some fairy-tale association association with hares, it doubtless originated as 'hairbell', since the flowers are carried on stems of hair-like fragility. Both French and Latin names refer to round leaves, remarkable for a plant whose obvious upper leaves are narrow and thread-like; but if you look at the base of the stem you will in fact find clusters of round leaves, like those shown in the smaller figure. This plant is also called the bluebell, or more accurately the blaebell, of Scotland, though the English bluebell, or wild hyacinth, also grows north of the Border. In Wales the harebell is poetically called *cloch yr eos*, the bell of the nightingale.

The harebell is a dweller amid the drier grassland of the downs and hills, where it opens it nodding trusses of flowers from July onwards. They vary a good deal in colour, shape and the number borne in each cluster. Unfortunately the harebell is a difficult plant to cultivate.

3

Bearded Bellflower

Campanule barbue *Campanula barbata*

This handsome campanula does not grow wild in Britain or America, though you may sometimes find it in gardens. It is common over all the Alpine regions of Switzerland, and also on the Carpathians and certain Norwegian mountains. There it grows on moist ground, especially amid the poor pastures of mat grass.

This plant's most striking feature is its pale blue, drooping flowers, bearing within them the long hairs that explain its name. Among the typical plants you may occasionally find ones with up-right flowers, deep violet blue in colour. This is called the variety *strictopedunculata*, but one can only surmise how and why it arises.

1
2
3
Hans Schwarzenbach 49

PLATE 6

Pink Family *Caryophyllaceae*

Ragged Robin

Fleur de coucou
Lychnis flos-cuculi

Red Campion

Lychnis rouge
Melandrium dioicum

1

Ragged Robin

Fleur de coucou — *Lychnis flos-cuculi*

The name of this dainty pink-flowered plant is singularly apt, for it can be told apart from other campions by its much divided, 'ragged' or laciniate petals. Such petals are a feature of its botanical family, the Caryophyllaceae, being found in many garden pinks and sweet williams.

'Robin' is a boy's name, associated perhaps with robin redbreast; it shows how country folk would sometimes personify a familiar flower or bird. The French and Latin names both mean 'cuckoo-flower', and were given because the ragged robin blossoms just when the cuckoo starts to call. In Welsh it is *cochyn bratiog*, the ragged red-fellow, or *blodeuyn y fran*, the crow's flower.

Remarkable features of the ragged robin are its strongly forked branching, its narrow opposite leaves with swollen bases that clasp the stem, and the swollen tubular red calyx of the flower. Flourishing amid damp meadows and woodland fringes, this gay flower studs the green of the grass with flashes of bright red. It is common throughout the British Isles, and over much of Europe and Asia.

2

Red Campion

Lychnis rouge — *Melandrium dioicum*

The red campion is a bold and sturdy plant that forms masses of rose-red blossom in open woodlands during May and June. In Wales it bears the curious name of *blodyn taranau*, flower of the thunders, possibly because it blooms when the thunderstorms begin.

Its much-branched stem is densely clad in somewhat glandular hairs. The flowers have a swollen calyx and curious petals. If you pass your finger nail over the blade of a petal, you will find at its base a pair of pale pink scales which, together with those of other petals, form an inner rim or coronella.

The flowers hang limply during the day, but raise themselves at eventide to attract the night-flying moths. As the Latin name suggests, red campion is dioecious, each plant bearing flowers of only one sex; but the rudiments of the other sexual organs are partially developed in every blossom. In the female flowers, a parasitic fungus which lives within the campion's anthers may cause the normal development of stamens. This results in hermaphrodite flowers, such as those in the picture. The presence of this fungal parasite is then revealed by the black colour of the anthers.

1
2

PLATE 7

Spindle Tree Family *Celastraceae*

Spindle Tree

Fusain d'Europe
Euonymus europaeus

Spindle Tree

Fusain d'Europe *Euonymous europaeus*

Though usually a low bush in thickets and hedgerows, the spindle sometimes becomes a small tree up to sixteen feet tall. It shows a strong preference for chalk and limestone soils, and is very common on the downs of the south and east, though scarce elsewhere. It is native to most of Europe and western Asia.

At the time of flowering in June it attracts no attention, for its flowers are small and greenish coloured. But it is most striking in autumn both for its fading wine-red foliage and its curious carmine red fruits. These are composed of four (or five) carpels which form a capsule having four (or five) blunt corners. As they ripen these fruits become even more conspicuous, for as they open they expose large hanging seeds, each surrounded by a fleshy, vividly orange-coloured aril. The whole fruit is generally held to be poisonous. Its peculiar shape has given this shrub the French name of *bonnet de prêtre* — priest's bonnet, and the German name of *Pfaffenhütchen*, priest's cap.

Another French name for this shrub, *bois carré*, or square wood, arises from the fact that its young green branches have four blunt brown corners, making each branch almost square in cross-section. The wood of the spindle tree is pale yellow, very hard, and suitable for turnery. The name 'spindle tree', like the French *fusain*, arises from the use of the wood, in earlier times, for making spindles on which women spun wool into thread. These were simple hand spindles, more primitive than the spinning wheel, and their use was widespread throughout Europe. The spindle whorls — small circular stones with holes through the centre, which were used to help twirl the wooden rod, are commonly found at most habitation sites.

In Wales, the spindle tree is called *pisgwydd*, or bladder-bush, from the shape of its fruits; and also *llwyn addurnol*, the ornamental bush.

Hans Schwarzenbach 49.

PLATE 8

Cabbage Family *Cruciferae*

Cuckoo Flower

Cresson des prés
Cardamine pratensis

Coral Wort

Dentaire bulbifère
Cardamine bulbifera

Cardamine heptaphlyla

Dentaire pinnée
Cardamine heptaphylla

1

Cuckoo Flower

Cresson des prés *Cardamine pratensis*

Everywhere, whether in Europe, Northern Asia or North America, the cuckoo flower laces the springtime green of damp meadows with its pale violet flowers. Its Latin name stems from the Kreek *Kardamon,* meaning cress, for it is edible and can be used in salads. Its English name tells us that it blossoms when the cuckoo comes, while from some legendary connection with the Holy Virgin it is also called lady's smock — more properly Our Lady's smock. The Welsh call it *bara can a llaeth,* white bread and milk, from the purplish-white colour of the flowers.

In the form of both leaves and flowers, the cuckoo flower shows remarkable variation. Thus, while all its leaves are compound, those arising near the base of the stem have small round leaflets, those higher up have large round ones while those still higher ave small and narrow. Occasionally plants are found with double flowers, formed by the stamens developing into petals. Such individuals are often wholly sterile, and can only increase vegetatively, by means of their creeping underground stems.

2

Coral Wort

Dentaire bulbifère *Cardamine bulbifera*

This elegant, violet-flowered cress is found here and there in damp open woods in the English Weald or the Chilterns, but is rare elsewhere. Its tall slender stems spring from a horizontal, branching, underground stem. From this stem also rise the large basal leaves, on long stalks, each with seven leaflets, whereas the leaves borne higher up the stem never have more than three or five. Within the leaf-axils, curious oval, violet-brown bulbils develop; these eventually fall off and germinate in the soil. There they immediately develop a root system, but the production of a flowering stem may take three or four years. This vegetative process of reproduction is the prevailing one, and hinders the normal growth of flowers and fruit-pods. Nobody knows just how this curious competition between flowers and bulbils has arisen. The name 'coral wort' or 'coral root' relates to the appearance of the white rhizome.

3

Cardamine heptaphylla

Dentaire pinnée *Cardamine heptaphylla*

This handsome plant is not native to Britain or America, but is common in European beechwoods in the Jura mountains, the Pyrenees, the Alps and the Apennines. The French name of *dentaire,* tooth-bearer, is well justified by the rhizomes, which are densely clad in large, short, tooth-shaped scales that take the place of radical leaves. The leaves that spring from the upright stems are compound and pinnate, the lower ones having three to four pairs of leaflets, and the upper ones two to three pairs. A cluster of flowers, thirty or more in number, surmounts the foliage; their colour ranges from pure white to pale lilac.

2
3
1
Hans Schwarzenbach 51.

PLATE 9

Teasel Family *Dipsacaceae*

Field Scabious

Langue-de-vache
Knautia arvensis

Small Scabious

Scabieuse commune
Scabiosa columbaria

Mountain Scabious

Langue-de-vache des montagnes
Knautia silvatica

1

Field Scabious

Langue-de-vache *Knautia arvensis*

The name 'scabious', is derived from the Latin generic name, *Scabiosa*, for certain species; some say the plant was so-called because it was used to cure *scabies*, the itch; others say that *scabies* is simply the roughness of the leaves. The French name, meaning 'cow's tongue', certainly records that roughness. This and related species provide some of our most charming garden flowers.

Field scabious, one of England's loveliest wild flowers, is only common on dry pastures in the south and east, especially those of the chalk downs. Its leaves are grass-green and hairy, the lower ones being more or less entire, and the upper ones much divided, with serrated edges. The stem leaves are cleft into three leaflets. The graceful flower stalks, often eighteen inches tall, bear hemispherical flower clusters like those of the Compositae, and likewise supported by an involucre of sepals. By contrast, the actual flowers differ. Each consists, in fact, of a long silky tube, united with an inferior ovary and an internal calyx. The four (not five) stamens exceed in length the four (not five) lobes of the corolla; they stand free — whereas those of Compositae are united with the tube as far the anthers. The florets around the edge of each flower head are expanded to give the appearance of a simple circular flower. The projecting stamens look like pins, and the whole flower head looks like a dainty lilac pincushion.

2

Small Scabious

Scabieuse commune *Scabiosa columbaria*

This species, more elegant than the others, is common on chalk and limestone soils, and amid sand dunes, in southern England. Its leaves, though often entire at the foot of the flower stalk, are much divided higher up, being split twice or thrice into narrow, pointed segments. Within the flower head, the calyx teeth end in long dark purple bristles, which are lacking in the genus *Knautia*, while the corolla has five lobes, not four (see the sketch). The dry fruit heads are almost spherical in shape. People sometimes gather them to feed canaries and other cage birds.

3

Mountain Scabious

Langue-de-vache des montagnes *Knautia silvatica*

To find this handsome scabious you must go to the forests and pastures of the mountains of Switzerland, and neighbouring European countries, for it does not grow wild in Britain or America. In its native home it flourishes as a characteristic member of the associations of tall herbaceous plants, and often stands three feet high.

The mountain scabious can be identified by the bright green shade of its leaves, which are either entire, or occasionally cut into segments at the base. Its stem leaves are always largest towards the base, whereas in the field scabious the stem leaves are larger towards the tip.

2
1
Hans Schwarzenbach 47
3

PLATE 10

Heath Family *Ericaceae*

Alpine Rhododendron

Rosage des Alpes
Rhododendron ferrugineum

Hairy Rhododendron

Rhododendron cilié
Rhododendron hirsutum

1

Alpine Rhododendron

Rosage des Alpes *Rhododendron ferrugineum*

The few European rhododendrons recall the Alps, and with good reason. They are essentially mountain dwellers confined almost entirely to the Alps, though a few grow also on the Pyrenees and the Apennines. Even Scotland can claim a dwarf mountain rhododendron, though it belongs to a separate genus, called *Loiseleuria procumbens;* it opens its pink blossoms on the slopes of the high Cairngorms, over 3,000 feet above sea level. The common garden rhododendron, *R. ponticum,* comes from Asia Minor, but the main home of this richly varied genus lies amid the Himalayan Mountains of East-Central Asia, where it numbers over 400 different species. The alpine rhododendron forms bushy tufts that seldom grow taller than three feet. Its supple branches carry, mainly at their tips, small leathery leaves which have their under-surfaces clad with closely adpressed scales. These are at first green but later assume the rust-red colour that gives the shrub its Latin names; their purpose is to restrict water-loss. The edges of the leaves are entire, and are rolled back — again a device to lessen transpiration. These leaves last for three or four years. The alpine rhododendron needs a peaty soil, but the underlying rocks may be either rich or poor in lime; in this respect it differs from our garden rhododendrons, which will not grow on lime-rich soils.

2

Hairy Rhododendron

Rhododendron cilié *Rhododendron hirsutum*

This close relative of the foregoing species is often considered inferior to it; but this is unfair, since it is just as lovely. The few real points of difference are not very obvious. The hairy rhododendron bears long hairs on the edges of its leaves, which are somewhat wavy. The undersides of its leaves bear scattered glandular scales, which give them a yellowish-green tint.

This species is confined to the central and eastern Alps, and its dependence on lime is shown by its absence from regions where limestone is wholly or largely lacking. It readily colonises screes and crannies in the rocks, which explains its common German name of *Steinrose,* literally 'rock-rose'. But is has no place in French folklore because it does not grow in the French-speaking regions.

1
2
Hans Schwarzenbach 48.

PLATE 11

Fumitory Family *Fumariaceae*

Hollow Corydalis

Corydale creuse
Corydalis cava

Hollow Corydalis

Corydale creuse *Corydalis cava*

The examples illustrated, one bearing red flowers and the other white ones, are both of the same species. It blooms in early spring, from March to April, and is often found forming colonies in thickets, parklands, broadleaved woodlands, or waysides, on fertile land throughout central and southern Europe.

The underground portion of this plant is a round tuber about the size of a nut, which in this species is hollow and so accounts for its name. The flower stem bears, all at one time, leaves and flowers, but all these wither as soon as the fruits ripen. So, from early autumn, the corydalis vanishes from the leafy carpet of the woodland floor.

The flowers, which bear long spurs, are visited by hive bees and bumble bees. Those insects that have long snouts go in through the gap between the petals; but those insects that have short snouts bite the side of the spur and in that way suck out the nectar secreted by nectaries close to the stamens. The stamens are set apart in a tightly shut chamber, and self fertilisation is rare, since the pollen of young flowers can only reach the stigmas of older ones. This arrangement helps to account fo the strange mixture of red-flowered and white-flowered individuals.

Though this species does not grow wild in Britain, we have four other charming native kinds.

1
2
Hans Schwarzenbach 51

PLATE 12

Gentian Family *Gentianaceae*

Purple Gentian

Gentiane pourpre
Gentiana purpurea

Spotted Gentian

Gentiane ponctuée
Gentiana punctata

1

Purple Gentian

Gentiane pourpre *Gentiana purpurea*

This handsome gentian, which in its general features resembles the one described below, is distinguished by its deep purple flowers. On their inner surfaces this colour passes gradually into yellowish shades dotted with red.
The purple gentian forms groups amid the Alpine pastures up to heights around 8,000 feet, but it also comes down into the conifer forests to play a part in the upper layer of tall herbs. Its natural range includes the Alps, the Apennines, and Norway, while it is also found in Kamtschatka; but everywhere it is unevenly spread. This is one of the herbalists' gentians, and from its roots, as from those of the large yellow gentian, there is extracted a drug used to cure stomach ailments.

2

Spotted Gentian

Gentiane ponctuée *Gentiana punctata*

The flower stems of this plant grow two feet tall, springing from a thick rhizome that also bears long underground roots. The leaves are set in opposite pairs, each pair being at right angles to the next; as a rule they are stalkless, but the lower ones may show short stalks; each leaf bears five prominent veins. The tubular flowers are grouped in showy clusters near the tip of the flower stem. Each corolla bears from five to eight rounded lobes. In colour it is pale yellow, studded with the many small dark violet spots that give the plant its name.
This species is common, and often grows in drifts, in the rocky meadows and dry grasslands of the Alps, and also amid the low shrubberies of rhododendrons. Cattle avoid it, as they do all the gentians, because of its bitterness. Geographically, it is confined to the Alps and the Balkan mountains, while it does not grow on limestone lands.

1
2
Hans Schwarzenbach 48

PLATE 13

Gentian Family *Gentianaceae*

Gentiana asclepiadea

Gentiane à feuilles d'asclepiade
Gentiana asclepiadea

Yellow Gentian

Gentiane jaune
Gentiana lutea

1

Gentiana asclepiadea

Gentiane à feuilles d'asclepiade — *Gentiana asclepiadea*

In this showy gentian, the flower stem, which grows from eighteen inches to three feet tall, is furnished with many pairs of pointed, oval leaves. Within the axils of the upper leaves arise the deep blue bell-shaped flowers, set singly or in pairs; each flower is studded on its inner surface with reddish violet spots. This species, which flourishes best in the limestone regions of the Alps, on moist or marshy meadows or amid shady woodlands, shows much variation in form. In sunny places it stands upright, and the leaves of each pair are directly opposite one another. But in shady spots its stalks are usually curved at the foot, and the leaves form two rows turned towards the light, while the flowers are likewise inclined. The name of *Gentiana asclepiadea* arises from the resemblance of its leaves to those of the swallow-wort or asclepias, a pungent medicinal herb that now bears the Latin name of *Vincetoxicum officinale.*

2

Yellow Gentian

Gentiane jaune — *Gentiana lutea*

The yellow gentian grows up to four or five feet tall, and can be found among the meadows of the Alps and the Jura, where it is often very abundant. It is happiest on limestone soils, and does not grow on granite rocks. After it has lost its flowers, it is sometimes confused with *Veratrum album* (see Plate 27); but the gentian has opposite leaves that are smooth below.

The yellow flowers are grouped in the axils of the upper leaves. They differ from those of the other gentians not only in their colour, but also in their shape. Each flower is deeply divided into five or six lobes, the points of which spread out into the form of a wheel.

The peasants dig up the roots, which are used for making extracts, tinctures, liquors, and salves, all alike employed against stomach ailments and digestive troubles, both in animals and mankind.

H. Schwarzenbach

PLATE 14

Geranium Family *Geraniaceae*

Herb Robert

Herbe-à-Robert
Geranium robertianum

Wood Cranesbill

Geranium des bois
Geranium silvaticum

1

Herb Robert

Herbe-à-Robert *Geranium robertianum*

This little cranesbill thrives everywhere, gaining a footing wherever man gives it a chance, on ruins, in clearings, and the sites of old bonfires. It makes itself at home along any hedge or in any wood where it finds enough moisture, shelter, and fertile soil. Nearly all Europe and Asia, along with the eastern side of North America and even parts of Africa, know it as a common wayside plant.

The flowers have five pink petals, bearing darker veins. They belong to the 'weather-wise' group. If the weather is fine, the stamens ripen first; but should the weather be bad, then it is the carpels that mature first, after the flower has opened.

As with all the cranesbills, each of the five husks of the fruit breaks away from the central axis by a sudden springing motion, from the base to the tip. It is thus flung for some distance, taking the seed with it. These husks stick readily to the hair of passing animals, who thus help to spread the seeds. But one cannot say whether it are the ants or other animals that carry the seeds on to roofs and walls.

2

Wood Cranesbill

Geranium des bois *Geranium silvaticum*

This showy plant has varied haunts according to where it grows. In the north of Europe, where Linnaeus gave it its Latin name, it forms part of the tall herb understorey of open pinewoods, sprucewoods, and birchwoods. In Scotland and northern England it is likewise a woodland plant, though it is found also in grassy and hearthery places. It is uncommon in Wales and Ireland, and unknown in southern England, but it reappears again on the mountains of central Europe. There, however, it is a grassland plant that thrives best in meadows — or in clearings. The flower stem is forked and bears on its upper portions a covering of glandular hairs; it bears leaves right down to the base. The large flowers, always set in pairs, have two whorls of stamens, with five stamens to each whorl; each whorl yields pollen at a different time. It is only after the inner stamens have shed their pollen, and have bent outwards, that the five stigmas spread themselves out for fertilisation. Thus, as Konrad Sprengel discovered as long ago as 1787, self-fertilisation is impossible.

The name cranesbill is derived from the slender pointed seed-pod, which resembles the beak of the heron — known locally in many districts as the crane.

1
2

PLATE 15

Iris Family *Iridaceae*

Yellow Flag

Iris faux-acore
Iris pseudoacorus

Siberian Iris

Iris de Sibirie
Iris sibirica

1

Yellow Flag

Iris faux-acore *Iris pseudoacorus*

This beautiful plant is widespread over Europe, and western Asia and has been introduced to North America. It lives in marshes, ditches, ponds, lakes and slow-moving streams where it often flourishes in the mass. Hence it is also called the marsh iris or water iris. You can grow it in your garden only if you own a pond, for unlike other common irises it must have its roots submerged.

The singular leaves of the yellow flag are flattened and curved like the blade of a sabre. The remarkable flowers have each a brief span of glory, falling after a few days, and they lack scent; but they have no equal either for form or for colour. The three outer petals are very large and reflexed, so that they hang downwards; hence they are called the 'falls'. The three inner petals which stand upright and are therefore called the 'standards' are, in this species, very small.

The pretty structure, at the heart of the flower, which appears to be made of petals, is in fact, a group of three peculiar stigmas, each of which is arched over in the form of a cap. Below each stigma, on its under surface about half way along, there stands a well-protected stamen. The receptive surface of each stigma forms a triangular patch set on its under-surface near the tip. The whole is so arranged that a visiting bee, forcing its way in to reach the nectar in the central peritanth tube, dusts into this receptive surface the pollen that it has brought from another flower. The bee then picks up a fresh load of pollen from the hidden stamen farther in, but as it backs out, the flower's own stigma is pushed back, and hence receives none of this pollen; in this way self-fertilisation is avoided. The stigmas lead down to an 'inferior' ovary in the centre of the flower, which ripens in autumn to expose bright orange seeds.

2

Siberian Iris

Iris de Sibirie *Iris sibirica*

This fine plant with its slender leaves and deep blue flowers, often forms splendid groups in marshy places or water meadows. Though it will grow below water, it is quite happy in moist soil, and hence can be grown in shady borders. It is not native in Britain or America, but flourishes across northern Europe and Asia as far east as Japan, and is now raised in water gardens in every temperate land.

In the Siberian iris the falls are not so large as those of the yellow flag, while the standards between them are large and have a bold curved outline. The petaloid stigmas each end in a double point, but nevertheless hold only one stamen. The delicate veining on the falls serves as a 'honey-guide' to direct the bees to the nectar. Higher up lies a patch of yellow hairs, which forces the invading insect up against the receptive surface on the under-surface of the stigma; and also against the hidden anther.

1
Hans Schwarzenbach 50
2

PLATE 16

Mistletoe Family *Loranthaceae*

Mistletoe

Gui
Viscum album

Mistletoe

Gui *Viscum album*

This plant is peculiar in every respect. Even its habit of growth is remarkable, for it consists of regular and repeated forked branching, with each terminal twig bearing two oblong leathery leaves. The joints of the stems are as green as the leaves, and likewise take part in the assimiliation of foodstuff from the air, with the help of their chlorophyll.

The yellowish-green flowers are inconspicuous. They arise in the forks of the terminal branches, and are of one sex only. In fact the whole plant is either male or female. The female plants ripen, towards the close of the year, their well-known white berries, each with a single seed enmeshed amid sticky slime. This stuff was in fact once used by fowlers as bird-lime, a practice now happily discontinued and illegal.

The thrushes, and particularly the mistle thrushes, eat the berries but reject the indigestible seeds. Some of these are planted directly on the bark of trees by the bird when it wipes its beak to rid itself of the troublesome pulp. Others pass right trough the bird's digestive system and emerge, with their germinative power unimpaired, to fall on the branches. Each seed then sends out a little horizontal root that bears sinkers, which work down through the bark to tap the upward sap stream for water and mineral foods.

The mistletoe is thus a partial parasite, and it can attack nearly all our broadleaved trees; poplar and apple are often affected, but oak seldom suffers. On the Continent, conifers are occasionally attacked, but only by special strains of mistletoe that are not found in Britain. Strangest of all, the mistletoe will sometimes parasitise itself, and instances have been found of a mistletoe plant of one sex growing upon one of the opposite sex, so that the whole 'plant' appeared bi-sexual.

Mistletoe growing on oak figured in the heathen rites of the ancient druids, and in Welsh it still is called *uchelwydd* — the highest tree of all. Nowadays we know it best as a kissing bough in constant demand at Christmas time.

Hans Schwarzenbach 44

PLATE 17

Mallow Family *Malvaceae*

Common Mallow

Mauve sauvage
Malva sylvestris

Hollyhock Mallow

Mauve alcée
Malva alcea

1

Common Mallow

Mauve sauvage — *Malva sylvestris*

One of the showiest of wild flowers, the common mallow springs up along waysides, streamsides, and the sea shore. It is found throughout Europe and northern Asia, and there are similar forms in America. The main stem of this sturdy perennial often reaches three feet tall. It bears rather ivy-like leaves usually divided into five broad lobes, but often more or less kidney-shaped; the dull red spot at the base of the leaf-stalk is characteristic.

The gay flowers are mauve-pink in colour, and it is indeed the French name for this plant that gives us our word 'mauve'. Their petals are blunt, or even heart-shaped, and bear a system of dark veins. The stamens are numerous, but united into a curious tube that completely surrounds the column of styles. At the foot of this column is a flattened ring of carpels, equal in number to the styles. When the fruit ripens, this ring breaks up into segments, each shaped like of piece of cheese. Country children call them 'cheeses' or 'cheese-cakes', and eat them, for they are quite wholesome.

Both the leaves and the flowers of the mallow have long been used in herbal medicine. They yield an insipid jelly which serves as a sweetener, a cough cure, or a poultice.

2

Hollyhock Mallow

Mauve alcée — *Malva alcea*

The hollyhock mallow is one of the finest of its attractive genus. It attains a height of three feet or more, and bears large blosoms that grow singly in the leaf axils on the lower part of the stem, but in clusters towards the tip. Its leaves are deeply divided into five irregular segments — a feature found also in one of the British native species, the musk mallow, *Malva moschata*.

In central and southern Europe the hollyhock mallow is often found along roadsides and hedgerows, or in vineyards. It is sometimes used in country medicine. We know it only as a rather striking garden plant. Its name records the resemblance of its flowers to those of the hollyhock, which belongs to the closely-related genus called *Althaea*.

1
2

PLATE 18

Willow Herb Family *Onagraceae*

Great Willow Herb

Epilobe hirsute
Epilobium hirsutum

Evening Primrose

Onagre bisannuelle
Oenothera biennis

1

Great Willow Herb

Epilobe hirsute *Epilobium hirsutum*

The Great or Hairy Willow Herb is one of the tallest, and certainly the largest-flowered, of many different species found wild across northern Europe and America. They are called willow herbs because their leaves resemble those of osier willows. The Latin name of *Epilobium* records the fact that their sepals and petals are placed above the ovary of the flower. Some species are small and inconspicuous, with small flowers. Others, like the Rose-bay Willow Herb, *Chamaenerion angustifolium*, form dense colonies in woodland clearings, and are very showy. A few grow in high mountains; one of these is the alpine willow herb, *Epilobium anagallidifolium*, which rises to a height of barely four inches in wet places among the northern hills.

But this Great Willow Herb is essentially a lowland plant, delighting in the rich soil of the lush water meadows. It is very common along the banks of the Thames and other southern English rivers. The Great Willow Herb sends up tall hairy stems to a height of three or even six feet. It spreads by means of underground runners as well as by the downy seeds that it releases to float on the wind.

2

Evening Primrose

Onagre bisannuelle *Oenothera biennis*

This handsome plant is a native of California. Introduced to Britain as a garden flower, it has now taken to the wilds. It remains rather local, however, and flourishes mainly on sandy dunes around seaside resorts, or on railway banks on the fringes of large cities. As the Latin name indicates, it is a biennial plant, though occasionally it completes its life cycle in a single season. Typically, during its first year of life it forms only a low rosette of leaves, and stores its food reserves in a fleshy taproot. Then in the second year of its life it shoots up a flowering stem, three feet or more in height. Once the fruits are ripe, the plant withers away completely, for it is reproduced only by seed.

The name of 'evening primrose' arises from its beautiful yellow flowers, which are generally shut during the day, but open towards evening to attract the night-flying moths. The French sometimes call this plant *cierge de nuit*, torch of the night, because of its hour of blooming. Its fleshy roots, if well cooked, taste delicious in a salad.

2
1
H. Schwarzenbach 44

PLATE 19

Poppy Family — *Papaveraceae*

Greater Celandine

Herbe aux verrues
Chelidonium majus

Corn Poppy

Coquelicot
Papaver rhoeas

1

Greater Celandine

Herbe aux verrues — *Chelidonium majus*

This plant grows chiefly on walls or amid ruins, especially in the shade, and rarely in mixture with native plants. Very probably it is a former cultivated plant that cannot hold its own away from the works of mankind. From any wound in the plant there springs an orange-yellow juice which has given it the reputation of a herb with many virtues. Even the alchemists of the Middle Ages pretended to see in its yellow root the philosopher's stone and the means of manufacturing gold.

Nowadays its reputation as a herb rests solely on the power of the juice to remove warts, provided it be applied with enough patience. Its French name means 'wart-herb'. The name of greater celandine comes from another French name, *grande chelidoine*, derived from the Latin *Chelidonium majus*, and ultimately from the Greek *chelidon*, meaning a swallow. The connection between bird and plant appears to be simply that the plant blooms when the swallow comes. But many more peculiar origins have been suggested, such as the fable that its orange juice restored the sight of blind swallows!

It is certain, however, that the greater celandine is poisonous, for it irritates the nasal membranes and causes vomiting. Its natural spread is due almost entirely to the ants, who hunt for its seeds. These seeds bear an oil-containing appendage which the little insects regard as a tit-bit. Thus the plant is one of those known as myrmecochores, or ant-attracters.

2

Corn Poppy

Coquelicot — *Papaver rhoeas*

Until quite recent years this vigorous plant was accounted one of the worst and most widespread weeds of European and American cornfields. But modern techniques of dressing seed corn to rid it of fine poppy seed, and the spraying of selective weedkillers, have brought it under control. It is now mainly a casual annual weed of the waysides, though occasionally, especially in East Anglia, the traveller may encounter the unforgettable sight of golden wheat studded with scarlet poppies. The corn poppy has a fascinating history. Its home was originally in Asia Minor, but it was carried everywhere by cultivators who could not separate its seeds from their corn. It reached Switzerland with the lake-dwellers, England with the New Stone Age farmers, and New England with the Pilgrim Fathers. The ancient Egyptians painted its flowers on their tombs.

The extremely fine seeds of the poppy have long been used as a spice on fancy cakes and buns. These seeds have to a mild degree the power of causing drowsiness. The petals have a similar property, and hence one German name for the poppy is *Kopfwehblume*, or headache-flower. In Wales its name is *pabi yr yd* — poppy of the corn.

A picturesque use for the blosoms is the making of poppy-dolls, called in France *petites madames*, or little ladies. The four red petals are bent back and tied with a blade of grass, to make the doll's skirt; then a straw is pushed crosswise through the seed-box to make a pair of arms and the doll is finished.

Hans Schwarzenbach 48.

PLATE 20

Polypody Family *Polypodiaceae*

Male Fern

Fougère mâle
Dryopteris filix-mas

Male Fern

Fougère mâle *Dryopteris filix-mas*

From ancient times this fern has been used as a remedy against tape-worms. The stump is the best source of the extract, especially if it has grown amid the hills, and has been gathered during August or September. The drug is not without its dangers, for too strong a dose is poisonous.

The male fern is a fine upstanding plant with fronds often three feet tall. It is essentially a dweller in shady woods and thickets. In Britain it is only really common in broadleaved woods amid the western hills; it needs a fertile soil and ample moisture, though it will flourish amid rocks; it is often associated with ash forest. In central Europe the male fern is less selective, though even there it prefers shady places facing northwards; in the Alps it ascends to 7,500 feet. A remarkably cosmopolitan plant, it is found in forests over most of the world, excluding however the arctic regions, the dry deserts, and the continent of Australia. In Wales it is called *rhedynen benyw* meaning, curiously, woman-fern.

In the Middle Ages everyone believed that this 'male' fern and the 'lady' fern, *Athyrium filix-femina* were the two sexes of a single species. But the essential features of sexuality among the ferns were not then properly understood; people hoped to recognise the male forms by their robustness, the female forms by their graceful habit. To-day we know that the spores of each fern, which is itself an asexual plant, give rise to a tiny, short-lived plantlet, called a prothallus. It is this prothallus which is the sexual stage, and it bears the reproductive cells of both male and female sexes. The fusion of these cells gives birth to an embryo, from which springs the fern as we know it. It produces in its turn the sprangia, or sporebearing bodies, below its fronds.

H. Schwarzenbach 50.

PLATE 21

Primrose Family *Primulaceae*

Oxlip

Primevère élevée
Primula elatior

Auricula

Oreille d'ours
Primula auricula

Yellow Loosestrife

Lysimaque vulgaire
Lysimachia vulgaris

1

Oxlip

Primevère élevée *Primula elatior*

This beautiful flower flourishes in a small zone on the borders of Suffolk, Essex, Cambridgeshire and Bedfordshire, where it is frequent in damp woods on clay soils. There it is an outlier from its mid-European home; varieties of it range as far afield as Asia Minor and eastern Siberia, while selected strains are grown in both British and American gardens. In lowlands, where it favours damp fields, streamsides, and waterside thickets, it blooms in April and May, before the leaves are on the trees. But up in the Alps, where it grows as high as 6,000 or even 7,500 feet above sea level, it delays its flowering until July or August.
Oxlip flowers, like those of most of the primrose tribe, are of two types. Some plants bear 'pin-eyed' flowers, in which only a long stigma is seen at the mouth of the corolla, while the short stamens lie hidden within. Other plants bear 'thrum-eyed' flowers, in which a cluster of stamens is seen at the corolla mouth, and the short stigma lies away out of sight. Insects tend to carry the pollen from one type of flower to the other, and in fact it only develops properly in a flower of the opposite kind to that which produced it.
This device, aimed at ensuring cross-pollination, is called 'heterostyly'.
Oxlip flowers are grouped in clusters of ten to twenty, not quite erect, but only inclined a little to one side, on a stalk from four to twelve inches long. Most oxlips produce no perfume, but a few are sweetly scented.

2

Auricula

Oreille d'ours *Primula auricula*

In Britain and America this delightful primula is known only as a cherished garden plant, but in Europe it is found as a spring-flowering alpine on the Alps themselves, the Apennines, the Carpathians, and also locally on the Jura mountains. Everywhere it prefers the limestone rocks.
Because of its delicate beauty, the early season of its flowering, and the abundance of its delicately scented flowers, the auricula has been gathered far too freely by heedless tourists. Hence the plant is now protected by law in many districts. The name 'auricula', like the French *oreille d'ours* or 'bears ear', is derived from the shape of the leaf, which suggests the ear of an animal.

3

Yellow Loosestrife

Lysimaque vulgaire *Lysimachia vulgaris*

Along the banks of slow-moving rivers threading lush pastures, the gay yellow loosestrife raises its showy wands of blossom around midsummer. Common in the south of England, it also flourishes all through the temperate zone of Europe and Asia.
The long flowering stem, often three or even four feet tall, bears leaves grouped in whorls of three or four; these leaves bear scattered reddish spots. The flowers spring from the leaf axils, in clusters of five or six. The green sepals and the yellow petals both stand free except at the base, where they are united in the tube so typical of the primrose family. The stamens are united, for half their length, in a curious yellow tube.

1
2
3
Hans Schwarzenbach 50.

PLATE 22

Rue Family *Rutaceae*

Dittany

Dictame commun
Dictamnus alba

Rue

Rue des jardins
Ruta graveolens

1

Dittany

Dictame commun *Dictamnus alba*

The curious names of this plant, in both French and English, are derived from the Latin *dictamnus*, which in turn comes from the Greek *diktamnos*, and signifies 'the plant of Mount Dicte'. The French also call if *fraxinelle*, the little ash tree, because of the shape of its leaves. It is a native of the south of Europe, including Greece and Italy, and does not grow wild north of the Alps. In Britain and America it is grown as a curious herb for the sake of its fragrant oil, which was used as a balm for wounds, or else it is sometimes cherished for its bright pinkish flowers. The flower stem and the veins of the leaves of the dittany are covered in black, stalkless glands; in these glands there develops the very volatile, and inflammable, essential oil. Its vapours accumulate all round the plant, especially on hot, windless days. They may reach the point at which a lighted match, skilfully applied in the evening, gives rise to a swift, bright flame that leaves the plant itself quite unharmed.

2

Rue

Rue des jardins *Ruta graveolens*

Though in no sense a showy plant, the rue bears pretty evergreen leaves, and still finds a place in gardens as a shrubby ornamental herb. Its small, greenish-yellow flowers, open in late summer. The whole plant yields a strong, rather unpleasant odour from all its green tissues. This is due to the presence of secretory glands which, in the leaves especially, can actually be seen as translucent dots. Oil of rue has some mild germicidal properties, and has proved effective as a dressing for sore eyes. Despite its strong taste, it has been used as a flavouring for drinks, while our forefathers ate rue leaves in salads, or strewed their living rooms with them to ward off the plague! The presence of such powerful oils is a common feature of the rue's botanical family, the Rutaceae, which includes the oranges and the lemons. Rue itself is found wild in most Mediterranean countries, and grows as far north as the southern valleys of the Alps, where it favours slopes among limestone rocks. It has long been cultivated, both in England and America.

Hans Schwarzenbach 48.

PLATE 23

Potato Family — *Solanaceae*

Henbane

Jusquiame noire
Hyoscyamus niger

Deadly Nightshade

Belladone
Atropa belladonna

1

Henbane

Jusquiame noire — *Hyoscyamus niger*

The ominous name of this curious plant suggests that it may kill poultry or wild fowl. It is of biennial growth, and is found in sandy places in Europe and southern England, often near the sea. The large leaves that spring from its three-foot stem are broken into broad, blunt-pointed lobes, two of which clasp the stem; they are densely clad in sticky hairs. The funnel-shaped, five-petalled flowers that cluster at the top of the stem are pale-yellow, with a network of purple veins, but change to a lurid reddish-violet at the centre. The fruit is an odd two-celled capsule, enclosed by the five-lipped calyx, with a lid that falls off when it ripens, to release the large black seeds.

The whole plant has a strong smell like that of tobacco, but far less pleasing. It is still grown as a crop, being raised from seed, and cut when it flowers in the second season; the leafy tops are then dried, and used medicinally as *hyoscyami folia*. Their active principles are two alkaloids, hyoscyamine and hyoscine, which have narcotic and hypnotic properties; they soothe the nerves, relieve pain, and cause drowsiness, but an overdose results in delirium, and even death. Henbane seeds were once smoked to relieve toothache.

2

Deadly Nightshade

Belladone — *Atropa belladonna*

This remarkable plant is found only on lime-rich soils in Europe and the south of England, where it forms dense clusters in open woodlands. It is a perennial that sends up a stout flower stalk, often four feet tall. It has large oval leaves, from the axils of which spring the bell-shaped flowers, of a purplish mauve hue. They soon ripen to black berries, which despite their collar of greenish bracts resemble cherries, and are sometimes eaten by children, with fatal results. Hence the plant's old name of 'dwale', connected with the Scots 'dule' and signifying sorrow.

The deadly nightshade is still grown commercially for the sake of its leaves, called *belladonnae folia*, and its roots, called *belladonnae radix*. Both contain two alkaloids, atropine and hyoscyamine. Atropine acts as a tonic to the nervous system, and has the singular power of causing certain organs to dilate. It is used in eye surgery, and it was its power of expanding the pupil that gave the plant its name of *bella donna*. For the beautiful ladies of Italy once enhanced their charms by using a tincture of its juice to make their eyes appear even more mysteriously large and alluring.

1
2
Hans Schwarzenbach 46

PLATE 24

Potato Family — *Solanaceae*

Thorn Apple

Pomme épineuse
Datura stramonium

Thorn Apple

Pomme épineuse *Datura stramonium*

This peculiar plant is accounted an alien in Europe and America, for it grows only under cultivation or on neighbouring waste ground. Its true home lies in Asia. It is a sturdy annual that grows rapidly to a height of three feet, and is eventually cut down by the frost.

Every part of the thorn apple is poisonous, but both leaves and flowers give off a smell so unpleasant that nobody would use them in salads. The rare cases of poisoning arise as a rule from the undue use of medicinal cigars or cigarettes which include the drug *datura* as a remedy for asthma.

The strong forked stem of the thorn apple carries groups of dark green leaves with bold wavy outlines. Within the axils of the leaves, and at the tip of the stem, arise the long, bell-shaped, conspicuous flowers, either white or purple in colour. They open only in the evening, and are pollinated by night-flying moths. The fruit is also remarkable: it looks like a horse chestnut; but it opens by four sections and bears at its base a little green collar, the remains of the calyx. Within this fruit lie many dark brown seeds, each somewhat flattened, and with a skin that is pitted with hollows.

Hans Schwarzenbach

PLATE 25

Daphne Family *Thymelaeaceae*

Daphne

Bois gentil
Daphne mezereum

Edgeworthia

Bois gentil japonais
Edgeworthia papyrifera

1

Daphne

Bois gentil *Daphne mezereum*

The delightful little daphne bush, so often cultivated in gardens, is native to the limestone fells of north-west England. In Europe it grows mainly amid forests upon lime-rich soils; in Switzerland it is found in the rhododendron zone, and ascends the slopes of the Valais to a height of 6,000 feet. Daphne is an under shrub, rarely more than three feet high, yet it has the erect form of a tree. Its lance-shaped leaves, which grow up to three inches long, appear only near the tips of the branches. The dainty, reddish-violet flowers, which are strongly scented, open in March, before the leaves have expanded. They give rise to scarlet berries that ripen in autumn.

These berries, and indeed the whole plant, hold a powerful poison. The sap of the daphne can in fact exert a blistering effect upon a sensitive skin. The Latin name of *mezereum*, sometimes expressed in English as 'mezereon', is a word of Arab origin that signifies poisonous. But the original English name was 'dwarf bay'. The name of daphne comes from the Greek, and means a laurel bush; it recalls the legend that the goddess Daphne was turned into a shrub.

2

Edgeworthia

Bois gentil japonais *Edgeworthia papyrifera*

This handsome shrub is cultivated in the south of Europe, England and the United States for its gay flowers and pleasing perfume. These flowers appear before the leaves, in clusters at the tips of the branches, and have at first a velvety, and almost a felted, aspect. At their first opening, they are golden yellow, but later they pale a little. The leaves, which appear later, are likewise closely clustered at the branch tips. At first they are velvety on both surfaces, but later they become smooth. In its native homeland of Japan, this shrub was once used for making paper, the pulp for which was obtained from its woody tissues.

Hans Schwarzenbach 44

PLATE 26

Valerian Family *Valerianaceae*

Common Valerian

Valériane officinale
Valeriana officinalis

Red Valerian

Centranthe rouge
Centranthus ruber

1

Common Valerian

Valériane officinale *Valeriana officinalis*

The old herbalists gave this plant its name, doubtless derived from the Latin verb *valere*, which means 'to keep well and in good health'. All the species of valerian hold, especially in their roots, an ethereal oil that was formerly used as a drug to cure nervous complaints. This oil, and therefore the whole plant, exerts a singular fascination over cats, who will often roll upon any crushed piece of wild valerian.

The valerian is a perennial with a short round root stock, from which springs a tall stem, from three to six feet high; it is usually unbranched below the inflorescence. This stem is furrowed, and carries compound leaves in opposite pairs. It ends in a showy flower cluster or corymb made up of as many as one hundred flowers. The corolla of each flower is bell-shaped, and has five petals and a rudimentary spur; it holds three stamens and an inferior ovary, with a single style. As the seed ripens, the calyx develops into a tuft of hairs, like that found in many plants of the related order Compositae; this helps to disperse the seeds.

The valerian grows throughout the temperate zone of Europe and Asia, but only on rich soils in damp places, such as streamsides and thickets beside rivers. In America it is cultivated as a herb.

2

Red Valerian

Centranthe rouge *Centranthus ruber*

This plant grew originally in the south-west of Europe, but it has long been introduced to America and northern Europe as a showy garden flower. It is now completely naturalised in the south and west of England, where it delights in lime-rich soils, and flourishes amid limestone quarries and on chalky banks, old ruins and sea cliffs. There are three colour varieties — red, rose, and white.

The flowers of this handsome plant have a narrow tubular corolla that bears a long thin spur. Each flower holds only one stamen. The young fruits are each topped by a crown of recurved bristles, derived from the calyx; the consequent hairy appearance of the whole inflorescence gives rise to the plant's common name of 'Jupiter's beard'. The leaves, borne in opposite pairs, are irregularly oval in outline, smooth-surfaced, and pale bluish green. The seeds of the red valerian are often dispersed by ants, who carry them into crannies in the rocks.

1
Hans Schwarzenbach 50
2

PLATE 27

Lily Family *Liliaceae*

Alpine Lily

Lis des Alpes
Paradisia liliastrum

Veratrum album

Vérâtre blanc
Veratrum album

1

Alpine Lily

Lis des Alpes *Paradisia liliastrum*

So handsome is this plant, that one is tempted to believe that it was given its Latin name to record a beauty fit for paradise. But in honesty we must admit that the name was created by an Italian botanist who wished to honour his friend, the Count Giovanni Paradisi, of Modena.

Nevertheless, the paradisia is a magnificent adornment of the alpine pastures. Though related to the lilies, it has no bulb, but a short underground rhizome. From this there spring the fine leaves, like blades of grass, and the tall leafless flower stalks, each bearing from five to fifteen blossoms. Here and there amid the Alps one may come upon meadows where this plant grows by the hundred nay, by the thousand, creating a magnificent scene. When viewed from afar it looks as though the whole ground is covered by a fresh fall of glistening white snow.

2

Veratrum album

Vérâtre blanc *Veratrum album*

This curious plant is common in meadows and clearings amid the mountains of central Europe, and its range extends to Siberia and Japan. It reaches a height of eighteen inches to three feet. Before the flowers open, the leaves are easily confused with those of the yellow gentian, but they differ in being alternately placed, velvety below, and strongly ribbed or pleated. The curious flowers, borne in a long raceme, are green with yellow stamens. Though so inconspicuous, they have in fact the same structure as the lilies and the tulips.

Cattle avoid the veratrum, because of its unpleasant taste, and the whole plant is regarded as poisonous to humans. But from its dried roots a powder is obtained which has been used in both human and veterinary medicine; it is very effective in promoting sneezing.

1
1a
2
H. Schwarzenbach 44

PLATE 28

Lily Family *Liliaceae*

Orange Lily

Lis orangé
Lilium bulbiferum

Turkscap Lily

Lis martagon
Lilium martagon

1

Orange Lily

Lis orangé — *Lilium bulbiferum*

This splendid lily, which reaches a height of three or four feet, grows wild in a few rocky places amid the Alps and the Jura, but is everywhere a rarity. In its few known haunts it enjoys special protection. It is well known, however, as a garden plant of great decorative value, both in Europe and in North America. The leaves of the orange lily are narrowly lanceolate in shape, and are borne in a dense whorl around the stem. Its bell-shaped flowers, bright orange flecked with black, are among the largest found on any European wild plant. In the garden strains these flowers are borne in a cluster of three or four at the top of the stem, but the wild race has but a single bloom on each stalk. On the wild kind, and also occasionally on the garden form, the curious bulbils that give the plant its Latin name may be found. They are small black structures that arise in the axils of the leaves and eventually fall off. They are capable of taking root, and thus the orange lily is not entirely dependent on seed for its reproduction.

2

Turkscap Lily

Lis martagon — *Lilium martagon*

The turkscap lily is reckoned the choicest of the smaller lilies commonly grown in British and American gardens. Its main home lies in Europe, where it is found in pastures and along woodland fringes at fairly low altitudes in the Jura and Alpine foothills; there, because it is so harassed by collectors, it enjoys special protection. It grows wild, too in a few woods in the south of England, but is very rare.

The stout stem of the turkscap lily, often three feet tall, springs from a bulb composed of yellow scales. This bulb is used in veterinary medicine under the name of *pomme d'or*, or golden apple. The stem bears rather sparse whorls of elliptical-lanceolate leaves. The purple flowers, spotted with black, are borne on drooping stalks. Their petals are bent back to a remarkable degree, so that the outline of the flower resembles a turban, and gives rise to the name of 'turkscap'. From the heart of the flower there project six stamens and a conspicuous, thick, black-tipped style. The stamens have large anthers supported centrally. At the slightest touch they shed large quantities of pollen, so aiding cross-fertilisation.

2
1
Hans Schwarzenbach 46

PLATE 29

Lily Family *Liliaceae*

Victorial Garlic

Herbe à neuf chemises
Allium victorialis

Didier's Tulip

Tulipe de Didier
Tulipa didieri

Snake's Head Fritillary

Fritillaire damier
Fritillaria meleagris

1

Victorial Garlic

Herbe à neuf chemises *Allium victorialis*

We have many species of wild garlic in our woodlands, but to see this peculiar kind you must go to higher mountain regions. It flourishes in stony places, below scrubby pine trees, amid the mountain thickets of the northern hemisphere. It is found from Spain to the Caucasus, and right across Siberia and North America. In Switzerland it grows from a height of 3,000 feet in the Jura to 7,500 feet in the Grisons.
During the Middle Ages the victorial garlic played a large part in popular superstitions. Anyone who possessed one of its rhizomes, or underground stems, was held to be safe against all misfortunes due to witchcraft. The reason for this odd belief lay in the many layers of fibres that cover the rhizome and its terminal bulb; country folk claimed that there were nine such layers, and nine was a magic number! Hence the French name, which means 'plant of the nine shirts'. If placed in a cradle, the root would scare away evil spirits, whilst in a cowshed it protected the beasts against enchantment.

2

Didier's Tulip

Tulipe de Didier *Tulipa didieri*

The tulips are scarcely known as wild plants, though a yellow-flowered species, *Tulipa sylvestris,* is occasionally found in English and Scottish woods. Most sorts come from the steppes of western Asia, but a few grow in southern Europe, and among these is Didier's tulip. It can be found in Switzerland in the fields and meadows of the Valais, sometimes wholly wild, or sometimes associated with cultivated fig trees, almonds, daffodils and irises.
This brilliant tulip is sometimes called *oeil-de-soleil,* or eye of the sun, for it holds within its scarlet corolla a star-shaped patch of a blackish blue shade. From this point there arise six dark purple stamens and a prominent pistil.

3

Snake's Head Fritillary

Fritillaire damier *Fritillaria meleagris*

This odd though charming plant bears peculiar names. Fritillary is derived from the Latin *fritillus,* a dice-box, from the box-like shape of the flower. The *damier* of the French name signifies a draughtboard, and is derived from the rectangular mottling of light and dark colours on the petals. The English 'snake's head' refers to the form and colour of the flower, on its drooping stalk, especially when only partially opened.
Most people know the snake's head best as a garden plant, though in England it grows locally in dense groups in water meadows beside the Thames and certain Suffolk rivers. Its range extends across central Europe and includes the flood-plain of the River Doubs in Switzerland. The colour of the flower varies from dark purple to white, the two colours being arranged in a chequerboard fashion, but garden strains include red, brown and blue also.

1
2
Hans Schwarzenbach 50
3

PLATE 30

Lily Family — *Liliaceae*

Grape Hyacinth

Muscari à grappe
Muscari racemosum

Nodding Star of Bethlehem

Ornithogale penché
Ornithogalum nutans

1

Grape Hyacinth

Muscari à grappe *Muscari racemosum*

This dainty little plant is one of several kinds cultivated in European and American gardens as attractive spring-blooming rockery flowers. It is native in England, but is rare, growing only on the Cotswold Hills or amid the Breckland heaths of East Anglia, where it flourishes in the dry, limerich grassland. It is also known as *Muscari atlanticum.*

The grape hyacinth sends up a solitary flower-stalk which carries a cluster of tiny dark blue flowers, very neatly arranged. The general shape of the flower head suggests a club, or perhaps the tassel of a drum. Each individual flower is bell-shaped, or rather urn-shaped, and its opening is edged with a white border. These flowers have a pleasant scent recalling that of a plum; those at the tip of the stalk are sterile. The fertile flowers ripen into little pods, at first pale green, then whitish and papery, which hold small black seeds. The leaves of the grape hyacinth are remarkably long and slender, and each leaf blade is incurved and furrowed. Below ground lies the pale brown bulb, which is usually surrounded by numerous bulbils; by their aid, the grape hyacinth spreads very freely in fertile garden soil.

2

Nodding Star of Bethlehem

Ornithogale penché *Ornithogalum nutans*

It is hard to say where this plant first arose — probably in the Near East. Its name tells of the legendary association of its star-shaped white blossom with the star that guided the three wise kings of the East to Christ's lowly cradle in the holy village of Bethlehem. It was introduced to Europe in the Middle Ages, perhaps by monks or crusaders. Then it was grown in the gardens of convents, from whence it spread over road-sides, fields, meadows, and vineyards. To-day it grows wild over most of Europe, but is every-where very thinly scattered. In America it is only a garden plant, one of several cultivated species of Star of Bethlehem.

Each separate flower of the Star of Bethlehem has six petals arranged in two whorls of three. These petals have a general greenish hue, but are milky white at their edges and in the centre. The stamens are peculiar, for they resemble a little tuft of petals at the heart of the flower. Each stamen consists of a broad flat pure white stalk, forked at the tip, holding an anther towards the middle.

The leaves of the Star of Bethlehem are exception-ally long, incurved, and furrowed. Together with the flower stalk, they spring from a brown-scaled bulb. The seeds are, without doubt, often dis-persed by ants. The flowers have the curious habit of closing at night, or when the weather is damp or the sky overcast.

1
2
Hans Schwarzenbach 51.

PLATE 31

Daisy Family *Compositae*

Adenostyles glabre

Adenostyle glabre
Adenostyles glabre

Adenostyles glabre

Adenostyle glabre *Adenostyles glabre*

This handsome alpine plant grows to a height of two feet or so, on rocky but rather moist ground, in ravines and forests up to the upper limit of tree growth. It seems to be restricted to lime-rich soils, and is only to be found in the Jura, the Alps, Corsica and Illyria. It ranges from 1,500 to 7,500 feet above sea level.

The leaves of *Adenostyles glabre* are boldly heart-shaped, edged with short evenly-spaced teeth. The little flower-heads, each normally composed of three tubular flowers, make up bold flower-clusters of a pink or purple hue. The layman can easily mistake each flower-head for a single flower. One vigorous plant bears from 200 to 400 flower-heads, which means from 600 to 1,200 actual flowers, each producing a single seed. Small wonder then that this plant is so abundant.

Hans Schwarzenbach 49

PLATE 32

Daisy Family *Compositae*

Carline Thistle

Carline sans tige
Carlina vulgaris

Carline Thistle

Carline sans tige *Carlina vulgaris*

The flower heads of this quaint plant attract attention by reason of their size — sometimes five inches across, by the beauty of their silver-white ray florets, and by their low stature. Although it sometimes grows a foot tall, the carline thistle often justifies its French name of 'stemless thistle' — represented by the words *sans tige* — by opening its blossoms almost at ground level. Strictly a plant of chalk and limestone soils, it is rare in England, though it flourishes on the dry pastures of the North Downs, where its dried-out blossoms and leaves sometimes survive the winter as a kind of 'everlasting' plant. But in fact it is a biennial which starts life in one year, stores foodstuffs in a fleshy root, and flowers and dies in its second summer.

The name 'carline' arises from a legend that one of the armies of the Emperor Charlemagne was saved from the plague by using this plant as a herb. In France the country folk call it the silver thistle, or the wild artichoke. The latter name arises from the fact that the base or receptacle of the flower head, if gathered when still young, is good to eat. Children eat it raw, and find it smacks of almonds and hazel nuts; but it tastes better when cooked like an artichoke, first boiled in salty water, then served with white sauce.

PLATE 33

Daisy Family *Compositae*

Woolly Thistle

Chardon des ânes
Cirsium eriophorum

Woolly Thistle

Chardon des ânes *Cirsium eriophorum*

The woolly thistle is a biennial plant. In its first year it forms no more than a basal rosette of leaves, which is remarkably decorative; they are displayed very regularly in such a way that none entirely covers another. These leaves, like those that spring from the flower stalk, are very deeply divided in a pinnipartite fashion, each segment in its turn being split into digitate segments, with the point of every segment prolonged to form a stout spine.

The flower stalk, which arises in the plant's second year, can grow almost as tall as a man. It is upright, strong, thick, woolly, much branched, and it carries flower heads that are two or even three inches in diameter. The bracts of the involucre, which are coarsely woolly, end in strong points. Altogether the whole plant seems to say 'Wha daur meddle wi' me!' Though the French call it the 'asses' thistle', it would be very foolish donkey indeed that tried to make a meal of it. The Welsh name is *ysgallen*.

This proud thistle, bearing clusters of rich purple florets upon its white flower heads, flourishes over most of Britain on sunny, stony pastures where its spines shield it from grazing livestock. You may find it too in clearings, on banks, and along the fringes of the wilder woods. It shows a liking for lime-rich soils, such as those of the chalk downs.

Hans Schwarzenbach 44

PLATE 34

Daisy Family *Compositae*

Elecampane

Grande aunée
Inula helenium

Elecampane

Grande aunée *Inula helenium*

The handsome elecampane, with its golden daisy-like flowers, is grown in both British and American gardens both for its beauty and its use in herbal cookery. Though native to England, it is rare as a wild plant, having possibly been over-gathered in the days when it enjoyed a great reputation as a cure for diseases of the chest. A perennial plant, it produces a fleshy root that is both aromatic and edible. This root was sometimes candied as a sweetmeat, while its aromatic oil was extracted and used to flavour liqueurs, such as absinthe. The whole plant, and especially the root, holds the carbohydrate inulin, which resembles starch but is soluble in water. When cultivated, the plant is increased by offsets, rather than by seed.

The elecampane was known to the Romans, and their name of *inula* occurs in the writings of Horace; *helenium* means 'sunflower-like'. The French name of *aunée* is a corruption of *inula*, and so, curiously enough, is the English 'elecampane'; for it arises from the Latin *inula campana* — the inula of the fields.

schwarzenbach 49

PLATE 35

Daisy Family *Compositae*

Sunflower

Tournesol
Helianthus annuus

Sunflower

Tournesol *Helianthus annuus*

Who would believe that this imposing plant, which grows up to ten feet in height and bears a flower sixteen inches across, is an annual? Today it is unknown outside the cultivated state, but its original home was, without doubt, Mexico and it was brought to Europe and the United States in the sixteenth century. It is very variable; the ray florets, usually golden yellow, may be lemon yellow, orange yellow, or even red; there are also double-flowered strains, which look not unlike the dahlias, to which the sunflower is related.

The sunflower grows from seed to maturity in a few months. It is cultivated commercially in Russia, East Africa, and Australia. One acre will yield fifty bushels of seed, from which as much as fifty gallons of oil can be extracted, at the rate of three gallons (or twenty-five pounds) of oil for every hundred pounds of seed. This oil, which is extracted under pressure, is yellow in colour and resembles linseed oil in its properties and uses; the oil cake that remains is fed to sheep, pigs, or poultry.

The seeds themselves are large and oval, but somewhat flattened; they are greyish, white, or black and white striped. They are harvested by cutting off the ripe flower heads, which are allowed to dry a little before the seeds are loosened by hammering with a wooden mallet. Even while the seeds are yet ripening, all sorts of seed-eating birds seek them out greedily. These seeds make a very good food for poultry, parrots, and pheasants.

Sunflower leaves can be used as fodder. The pith of the sturdy stems is one of the lightest substances known, having a specific gravity of 0.03, compared with 0.09 for the pith of elder stems, and 0.24 for cork. When the crop is grown on a large scale, the stalks are burnt as fuel, and their ash, which is rich in potash, is returned to the land.

The peculiar habit of the flower heads, in turning always to face the sun, has earned the sunflower a variety of names, with similar meanings, in different languages. Thus we have the Latin *helianthus*, the French *tournesol*, the German *Sonnenblume*, the Greek *heliotrope*, and the Italian *girasole*.

Hans Schwarzenbach 49.

PLATE 36

Daisy Family *Compositae*

Yellow Camomile

Camomille des teinturiers
Anthemis tinctoria

Tansy

Tanaisie commune
Tanacetum vulgare

1

Yellow Camomile

Camomille des teinturiers *Anthemis tinctoria*

The stiff stems of this perennial plant grow from six to twenty-four inches tall. They are much branched, and carry feathery, doubly-divided or bipinnipartite leaves, very regularly arranged. These leaves bear a silky down on their under surfaces. The flower heads appear at the end of long leafless stalks. The bracts of the involucre are woolly, and form a cup around the hemispherical cluster of florets.

The flower-heads are always golden yellow, with from 30 to 35 ray florets around the rim and from 300 to 350 disc florets crowded into the centre. Between the florets, on the surface of the receptacle, stand narrow, stiffly-pointed bristles. Originally native in western Asia, the yellow camomile is now widely distributed across central and southern Europe, and frequently grows wild as an 'escape' in England and America. Its introduction dates from its uses, in earlier times, as the source of a yellow dye. The French name of *camomille des teinturiers*, or 'dyers' camomile', records this; it is also called in France the *oeil-de-boeuf*, or bull's eye. It flourishes best on the dry sunny banks that resemble its native steppes, and it prefers limerich soils.

2

Tansy

Tanaisie commune *Tanacetum vulgare*

Tansy is a sturdy perennial that grows from one to three feet tall. From a branching underground stem it sends up several stout furrowed stalks which divide into branches towards the tip. The dark green leaves have a feathery form, being doubly divided or bipinnatifid. The numerous flower-heads are grouped into clusters, simple or compound, in such a way that those of each cluster stand on a level. In effect each flower head consists only of disc florets, for those on the rim have no ray petals, or only very short ones.

In England tansy is a widespread but rather local plant, which flourishes along river banks, but also grows on roadsides, railway banks, walls, and waste ground generally. In America it is cultivated occasionally as a herb, though it is now considered more decorative than useful. The whole plant is pervaded by a sharp aroma which led to its being gathered for shredding, and so prepared it was used as flavouring for cakes, puddings, omelettes, or stews, for garnishing salads, and even in herb teas. Oil of tansy is still employed in perfumery, while its dried leaves have insecticidal powers. The herb's greatest value, however, was as a remedy for internal worms, both in humans and livestock. Hence the French folk name, *herbe-aux-vers*, or 'worm-plant'.

Hans Schwarzenbach 50

PLATE 37

Daisy Family *Compositae*

Mountain Hardhead

Bluet des montagnes
Centaurea montana

Cornflower

Bluet
Centaurea cyanus

1

Mountain Hardhead

Bluet des montagnes *Centaurea montana*

This beautiful perennial is often cultivated in rockeries and herbaceous borders, both in Britain and America. Its home lies amid the limestone hills of central Europe, where it flourishes on sheltered well-drained slopes, both on pastures and in the undergrowth of the forests.

Its sturdy flower stalk bears large lance-shaped leaves, with margins that run down the stem; that is to say, they are decurrent. The flowers are rather like those of the cornflower, but are larger and less regular. Each flower head bears a sprinkling of showy florets, which are sterile and serve only to attract the insects to the smaller fertile florets below them. Within these fertile florets, the stamens have a curious mode of action. At the least touch, such as that of an insect's snout, the inner face of each staminal filament contracts. Since the pollen sacs are joined, the whole ensemble makes a sliding movement against the base of the pistil. During this time, the pollen pours out internally, so that when the stamens return to their original position as the insect leaves, the pollen is brushed effectively against it.

2

Cornflower

Bluet *Centaurea cyanus*

The aptly-named cornflower was originally a native of the steppes and rocky hillsides of the Mediterranean lands, from Sicily to the Near East. But the farmers of the New Stone Age were unable to separate its seeds from their wheat grains, and so they carried it first to the Swiss lake dwellings and later to their settlements all over Britain. Later it was again carried overseas by the first settlers in New England. For centuries it grew brightly amid the corn but modern methods of seed dressing have now eliminated it from the crops. Nowadays you are most likely to find it on waste ground, or as an escape from a garden.

The flower heads of the cornflower bear two sorts of florets. The outer ones are shaped like open bells, with prettily displayed petals; but they are sterile and serve only to attract insects. The inner fertile flowers, though likewise blue, are inconspicuous. The colouring matter of the petals is an anthocynin pigment, which turns blue while the sap is alkaline, but red when it is acid. This explains the colour range of garden cornflowers, from red through purple to dark blue and pale blue.

Hans Schwarzenbach 48.

PLATE 38

Daisy Family *Compositae*

French Hardhead

Jacée des prés
Centaurea jacea

Chicory

Chicorée sauvage
Cichorium intybus

1

French Hardhead

Jacée des prés — *Centaurea jacea*

This very showy relative of the common hardhead, or knapweed, rare in Britain, is common in France and Switzerland, where it grows abundantly in both damp and dry meadows, pastures, on verges and on newlyformed shingle beds. Anyone who gathers specimens from such varied places will find that none are quite identical which has forced the botanists to divide the species into many sub-species, varieties, or forms. Some of these are tall and slender, others short and squat: some are freely branching, others scarcely branched at all; the flower heads may stand singly or in groups; the leaves in particular show great diversity, from simple entire blades to deeply cut and divided forms. Each strain may again be differentiated by the bracts that form the involucre below the flower head. Each bract consists of a green base supporting a rough, brownish, well-defined upper portion, which may have an edge entire, more or less broken, or even fringed; these bracts are a characteristic feature of the hardheads and cornflowers. The outer florets are nearly always far larger than the others, but are always sterile, forming an attractive cloak for the fertile florets within.

2

Chicory

Chicorée sauvage — *Cichorium intybus*

In the height of summer, along roadsides and in dry fields, one often finds this sturdy plant growing two or three feet tall, with spreading branches and magnificent pale blue flowers. It is native to Europe, and possibly to England, and was long ago introduced as a cultivated crop to North America. The lower leaves of the chicory are rather like those of a dandelion, long and slender, with irregular edges; the upper ones are shorter, heart-shaped or arrow-shaped, and sit directly on the stem. The flower heads are numerous, and are placed either within the axils of the branches or at their tips. They open late in the morning, and close again in the late afternoon. All their florets are of the showy ray form.

In the Middle Ages, chicory played a part in witchcraft; it was supposed to have magic powers to ward off evil and to ensure love and happiness. One legend maintains that the wild chicory is an enchanted maiden who waits eternally by the roadside for the return of her sweetheart, called away to the wars.

Cultivated chicory is used in three different ways. Much is grown as a root crop, especially in Europe. The roots, which are a foot long and two inches thick, and weigh up to half a pound, are cut into slices, roasted, and ground to form a brown powder. This is used to blend with coffee, or even on its own as a refreshing beverage. Alternatively, the roots are used for forcing into growth, in total darkness, the white rosettes of leaves that comprise the chicory of salads. The third use is as a fresh green salad, and for this purpose the related, endive, *Cichorium endivia*, is usually preferred, as its more ragged leaves are less bitter.

1
2
Hans Schwarzenbach 46

PLATE 39

Daisy Family *Compositae*

Alpine Lettuce

Laitue des Alpes
Cicerbita alpina

Alpine Lettuce

Laitue des Alpes *Cicerbita alpina*

This is a magnificent and imposing plant, as high as six feet tall. It flourishes for preference in the damp and shady hollows of the mountain forests, amid the upland thickets of alders and dwarf pines, across most of the mountain ranges of central and western Europe. It appears to prefer lime-rich rock formations.

The large leaves of the alpine lettuce are noteworthy for the angular bays along their edges, for their very large triangular terminal lobe, and for their heart-shaped base. The flower heads are numerous, and stand on long stalks. Each consists of about twenty violet blue florets, and the whole ensemble is most effective.

Every stem of the plant, and even the bracts below the flower heads, appear shaggy with glandular red-brown hairs.

The alpine lettuce thrives well in parks and gardens. It is related to the flea-banes of the genus *Mulgedium*. The name 'lettuce' derives from its milky sap, in fact the very word lettuce is derived from the Latin *lac* for milk.

Hans Schwarzenbach 51

PLATE 40

Daisy Family *Compositae*

Dandelion

Pissenlit
Taraxacum officinale

Dandelion

Pissenlit *Taraxacum officinale*

In April, and even more so in May, the dandelion blooms in such profusion that the gorgeous golden yellow of its flowers gleams from afar among the meadows, especially on sunny days. Few plants have so many names. It is called pissabed, or in French *pissenlit,* because of its diuretic properties. The name of dandelion, from the French *dent de lion* or lion's tooth, was given it because of the pronounced toothed edges of its leaves. Other names in France are *salade des taupes* or mole's salad, *laitue des chiens* or dog's lettuce, and *couronne des moines* or monk's crown. The Welsh name is *dant y llew* — tooth of the lion.

Children make chains and coronets from its leaves and flowers, and whistles from its stems. They blow away the winged seeds from its ripe flower-heads, and pretend to tell the time thereby, and this custom has earned it yet another name — the 'four o'clock'. It is because of these winged seeds that the dandelion has spread so far and wide — virtually over the whole world.

In springtime the fresh young leaves make a delectable salad, though this is more popular on the Continent than with us. The fleshy roots are sometimes roasted and ground, to give a substitute for chicory or coffee, or to mix with those beverages.

In herbal medicine, both leaves and roots are used in decoctions and infusions as purifying drugs or diuretics, or to ease stomach troubles. In some countries the flowers are still made into a sweetmeat or jelly that is most effective against sore throats.

H. Schwarzenbach 44

PLATE 41

Buttercup Family *Ranunculaceae*

Marsh Marigold

Populage des marais
Caltha palustris

Fine-Leaved Peony

Pivoine à feuilles menues
Paeonia tenuifolia

1

Marsh Marigold

Populage des marais *Caltha palustris*

You may find this beautiful ally of the buttercup along watersides in nearly every country of Europe, northern Asia, and North America. In its commonest form it is a lowland plant, but there are local races, characterised by their creeping stems which root at the joints, that grow far up into the mountains — up to 3,000 feet elevation on the Cairngorm range of Scotland. The marsh marigold prefers the more fertile and less acid swamps, such as those where alders flourish. It is happy too along river banks, and in those boggy patches of low-lying fields to which streams or springs bring constant fresh water and mineral nutrients.

Its bitter taste protects it from the attacks of cattle, but it is often gathered for its beauty when it opens its golden blossom in April and May. The marsh marigold passes the winter as a stout underground stem, which gives rise to leaves and flower stalks as soon as the swamps start to warm up in spring. Its lower leaves have long stalks, but the upper ones are short-stalked or else clasp the stem; all the leaves have somewhat wavy edges. In the flower there is no distinction between sepals and petals, and the bright gold petal-like members are the outermost part of the bloom; there are no nectaries.

Another common name for the marsh marigold is 'kingcup'. In Wales it is called *gold y gors*, golden flower of the bog, or else *crafanc y fran*, crow's claws, from the shape of the seed pods.

2

Fine-Leaved Peony

Pivoine à feuilles menues *Paeonia tenuifolia*

This magnificent plant, a native of Siberia, is occasionally cultivated in gardens. It is nearly always a single-flowered plant, bearing five or six intensely red petals above a calyx of five green sepals. Numerous golden yellow stamens stand out brightly at the base of the shiny corolla. In our gardens we grow a large number of allied peonies, mostly forms of *Paeonia mascula* (also called *P. officinalis*). A wonderful range of white, pink, red and purple varieties, including some with double flowers, has been developed. The apparent 'doubling' of the petals is in fact due to the transformation of certain stamens into petals. The wild peony of the cliffs on the island of Steep Holm in the Bristol Channel is a single-flowered strain of *Paeonia mascula*. Its stands up to two feet high, bears large, dark green shiny leaves, and has glorious deep red flowers, often four inches across, which open in June.

Hans Schwarzenbach 50

PLATE 42

Parsnip Family *Umbelliferae*

Hogweed

Berce
Heracleum sphondylium

Hogweed

Berce *Heracleum sphondylium*

The beauty of this grand plant often goes unrecognised as it is so common and occurs in such large groups. Everywhere, amid green and fertile fields, damp woodland glades and hollows, and in moist spots along the roadsides, it springs up each summer as a commonplace feature of the landscape. Let us look at it in detail. Its hollow stem, often five feet high, is finelly channelled, recalling the Doric columns of a Grecian temple. The leaves show many expressions of sculptured shapes — the large expanse of the central leaflet, the curious basal sheath, the uneven segmentation, and the irregularly toothed borders. Their resemblance to an acanthus leaf, they recalls a motif of the Corinthian order.

As for the flower heads or umbels, each composed of from fifteen to thirty lesser flower heads or umbellets, which form a real poem of plant life. Mathematically they are a perfect example of the use of space; despite a diversity of individual flowers, they build up a united whole. The corollas of each separate flower adapt themselves geometrically to the available space; they get larger and larger as one goes from the centre of each umbellet towards its circumference. Moreover, within each individual flower, it is the outer petals that are the best developed. So they build up into a marvellous composition, looking like a single giant blossom, wherein the smallness of each part is offset by the perfect relationship of hundreds of them to each other.

This white globe of blossom attracts a large number of insects, and beekeepers well know the hogweed's value as a source of nectar. In fact, at the height of summer a large part of all the honey that the hives produce is gleaned from this and similar umbelliferous plants. The hogweed is also called the 'cow parsnip', though cattle are not particularly fond of it. Its leaves yield excellent green fodder for tame rabbits, while its dead flower heads are sometimes gathered in winter for use in decorative floral arrangements.

Hans Schwarzenbach

PLATE 43

Buttercup Family *Ranunculaceae*

Mountain Pasque Flower

Pulsatille des montagnes
Pulsatilla montana

Alpine Clematis

Clématite des Alpes
Clematis alpina

1

Mountain Pasque Flower

Pulsatille des montagnes *Pulsatilla montana*

This choice springtime blossom is often found in the warm dry valleys of the Valais and the Grisons, but is scarce elsewhere. It is classed among the anemones because of its regular perianth of pinkish blue petals, its cluster of many golden yellow stamens, and the numerous free carpels at the heart of the flower. The structure of its fruit, which is a tuft of single-seeded achenes ending in long spines, show that it belongs to the genus *Pulsatilla*. The flower stem bears three remarkable bracts, and much divided silky in texture, which tend to become red; at first they are closely adpressed to the flower, but by the time the fruit is ripe they have become separated from it by reason of the extending fruit stalk.

Very similar to the species illustrated is the wild English pasque flower, *Pulsatilla vulgaris*, which grows sparingly amid the turf of dry chalk and limestone hills between the Thames and the Humber. It draws its name from the fact that it blooms at Easter. Both make delightful rockery plants.

2

Alpine Clematis

Clematite des Alpes *Clematis alpina*

Because its twining stem clings to any sort of support, and because of the shape of its divided leaves, the peasants of France and Switzerland often call this pretty climbing plant a 'vine'. But as soon as it flowers, its true identity is apparent, for its showy blossoms are quite unlike the tiny inconspicuous flowers of the grape vine. The perianth of the clematis consists of four petals, shaded metallic blue or violet, within which there are several white false petals or staminodes, which bear nectar. Within these again lie numerous stamens and carpels, all of which latter develop, at the fruiting stage, into achenes or singletseeded bodies each topped by a tuft of feathery plumes. The twining leaf-stalks help the plant to climb. Each separate leaf is divided into three groups of three leaflets each. This plant is commonest amid the scrub of the rocky foothills of the Alps.

Closely allied to this alpine clematis is the English traveller's joy, *Clematis vitalba*, also called the 'virgin's bower' because of the dome-shaped thickets it sometimes forms, and 'old-man's beard' by reason of its masses of feathery seeds. Its flowers, are greenish-white and inconspicuous. This species only grows wild on chalk and limestone, but it is used by nurserymen everywhere as a stock for grafting the many choice varieties of cultivated clematis.

2
1
Hans Schwarzenbach 46

PLATE 44

Buttercup Family *Ranunculaceae*

Windflower

Sylvie
Anemone nemorosa

Hepatica

Anémone hépatique
Hepatica triloba

1

Windflower

Sylvie *Anemone nemorosa*

This dainty and delicious spring flower carpets the floor of English oakwoods with drifts of nodding blossoms in March and early April. It is one of the pre-vernal woodland plants, which open their leaves while the trees above them are yet bare, so as to enjoy the spring sunshine before it is intercepted by the forest foliage. The slender whitish stem springs from a dark brown underground rhizome, in which the plant's food reserves are stored during the winter. The leaves, few in number, are divided into five leaflets, which in turn have a number of lobes. The pretty flowers are dark pink on their outer surface, and at night or in stormy overcast weather the flower stalks bend over so that the inside of the flower is shielded from wind and rain.
When fully open, the windflower shows six white petals, a cluster of numerous yellow stamens and a group of free green carpels in the centre. It is essentially a woodland plant, and if it grows on upland pastures it is only as a relic of woods cleared not long ago.

2

Hepatica

Anémone hépatique *Hepatica triloba*

The name of this plant is derived from the Greek work for liver, *hepar*, because in ancient herbal medicine it was used as a supposed cure for liver troubles, on the basis of the slight resemblance of its leaves to that organ. In Central Europe it is widespread amid broadleaved forests and scrub, and on stony slopes. Occasional plants can be found in the sub-alpine zone, usually on sandy or on lime-rich soils. In Britain, however, we know it only as a rock-garden plant.
Though the pretty mauve-coloured flower of the hepatica lacks nectar, it produces abundant pollen. Hence it is much visited by bees, some beetles, and those butterflies that feed on pollen. Its petals close up during the night, and also in rainy weather. In days gone by this plant was used for making herb teas.

1
2
HANS SCHWARZENBACH 44.

PLATE 45

Buttercup Family *Ranunculaceae*

Aconitum paniculatum

Aconit paniculé
Aconitum paniculatum

Aconitum paniculatum

Aconit paniculé *Aconitum paniculatum*

This handsome plant is native to Central Europe, where it flourishes mainly on shady slopes, in the mountain forests and ravines. There, amid a rich vegetation of shrubs and tall herbaceous plants, it rises to a height of four to five feet. It bears lobed leaves divided into from five to seven segments, themselves deeply cut; its branching flower stalks carry panicles or spikes of violet or deep blue blossoms.

These flowers are remarkable for the form of the upper petal, which is curved, bent over, and flattened sideways, assuming the shape of a helmet. If you lift this up gently, you will find beneath it two other remarkable structures, in the form of little helmets borne on long stalks, yet hidden within the larger one. Within these peculiar bodies lie the nectaries, which secrete the sweet nectar that is held on their upper tips, which are lightly bent over. The bumble bees, which are the principal insect visitors to this flower, come here to gather the nectar.

However, certain bumble bees, those having only short snouts, cannot reach it in the normal way. They find that the opening of the helmet is too narrow to let them thrust themselves right into the flower, and hence they cannot plunge their tongues into the long-stalked 'honey-pots'. So they satisfy themselves by biting a hole through the outside of the upper surface of the helmet, at the very point where the nectaries lie. Nothing then stops them from enjoying the sweet contents. By so doing, these bumble bees do not assist in the fertilisation of the flowers, which however also practice self-fertilisation.

Two other plants closely resemble this species, and both are aptly called 'monkshoods' from the shape of their flowers. One is the English wild monkshood, *Aconitum anglicum*, which grows sparingly along shady streamsides in the West and Midlands of Englands, and in Wales. The other is the garden monkshood, a European species cultivated in England and America, *A. napellus*, which also prefers moist situations. All these plants are very poisonous.

The Welsh name for monkshood is *Adda ac Efa* — Adam and Eve, because one flower can apparently be found within the body of another one.

Hans

PLATE 46

Buttercup Family *Ranunculaceae*

Delphinium

Dauphinelle élevée
Delphinium elatum

Aconitum lycoctonum

Aconit tue-loup
Aconitum lycoctonum

1

Delphinium

Dauphinelle élevée — *Delphinium elatum*

This is the wild form of the tall cultivated delphiniums that make so brave a show in gardens throughout Europe and North America. There are to-day countless varieties of them, coloured pale or dark blue, mauve or purple, pink or white, or patterned perhaps in two such shades; the varieties differ too in flower structure and height. The wild race flourishes on the Alps and other mountain ranges of central Europe, and also in Siberia and central Asia. Its grows on alpine pastures, or else, below the 6,000 feet contour, forms a part of the association of tall herbaceous plants in and around the forests, Its flower spike is often over four feet tall, and it is a perennial, springing up from a fleshy root-stock year after year.

The flower structure delphinium's is peculiar. Five blue petals surround the numerous stamens and the pistil. One of these petals, the upper one, is drawn out into a long upturned spur. Then follow four blackish-brown nectar bearing members; two of these are turned upwards and are also spurred; their spurs open towards the surface where they meet, supporting themselves at this point, and lying enclosed within the larger petaloid spur as though in a sheath.

2

Aconitum lycoctonum

Aconit tue-loup — *Aconitum lycoctonum*

This delicate yellow-flowered ally of the monkshood grows in Central Europe. In the past, these flowers, because of their poisonous properties, were used to kill dangerous beasts, and particularly wolves. Hence the French name of *tueloup*, or wolfs-bane.

The monkshoods can be known by the helmet-like shape of their outermost upper petal, which in this species is remarkably well developed. Its floral structure resembles that of the other monkshoods, previously described. As with those flowers, it is designed to make visiting bumble bees enter below the helmet, but this species too sometimes suffers from bees that bite their way in through the petals to get at the nectar.

2
1
Hans Schwarzenbach 50

PLATE 47

Buttercup Family *Ranunculaceae*

Stinking Hellebore

Ellébore fétide
Helleborus foetidus

Winter Aconite

Eranthe d'hiver
Eranthis hyemalis

1

Stinking Hellebore

Ellébore fétide *Helleborus foetidus*

What a horrid name for such an elegant and distinguished a plant! Its lower leaves spread themselves like picturesque fans, forming a pedestal for the flower stems so richly laden with blossom. The whole ensemble suggests the silhouette of a lady clad in a crinoline, but nevertheless sodden with scent, for the whole plant gives off the nasty smell that accounts for its name. In actual fact this stench comes mainly from special glands on its leaves and stems. The leaves, incidentally, are evergreen.

The flowers, though green, have their attractions, especially as they flourish in the depths of winter. They are bell-shaped, and edged with deep red; within lie many stamens, then a pistil. Around the stamens there is a remarkable coronet of greenish, nectar-bearing members, shaped like funnels.

The stinking hellebore is a typical plant of chalk and limestone country, and its main home is in south-west Europe. In Switzerland it is only found in the more oceanic regions of the Jura and the Alps. In Britain it is native only to the South of England and South Wales, occurring now and again in thickets on the lime-rich rocks.

2

Winter Aconite

Eranthe d'hiver *Eranthis hyemalis*

As soon as the least rise of temperature allows, even in the heart of winter, the aconite blooms, heralding too soon the coming of the spring. It is the very earliest of the pre-vernal woodland flowers, which enjoy the sunlight on the forest floor before the tall trees above them have spread their foliage. Both its leaves and its flower stems spring directly from the brown underground corm wherein it stores its food supplies from one season to the next.

The winter aconite can at once be recognised by the frill or ruff of green sepal-like leaves that surround its flower. The petals, which together form an open chalice of golden-yellow hue, are each accompanied by a small, inconspicuous, nectar-bearing member, whereas the petals of the buttercups themselves bear nectaries. The whitish, fleshy flower stalk stands from four to six inches high. The flower is soon succeeded by a curious fruiting head, composed of several, diverging, dark brown seed pods. The leaves fade and die before midsummer, and the plant then sleeps below ground until next spring.

Southern Europe, from France to Serbia, is the homeland of the winter aconite. But in both Britain and America it is widely cultivated as a garden flower, propagated by its dried, irregularly shaped corms which can be planted like bulbs in autumn. Here and there it has become naturalised in shrubberies, hedgerows, and woodlands, and has gone thoroughly wild.

1
2
Hans Schwarzenbach 53.

PLATE 48

Buttercup Family *Ranunculaceae*

Green Hellebore

Ellébore vert
Helleborus viridis

Lesser Celandine

Ficaire
Ranunculus ficaria

1

Green Hellebore

Ellébore vert *Helleborus viridis*

Like the other hellebores, this green species has dangerous narcotic and poisonous properties, and like them too it shows singular peculiarities of form. Its large basal leaves are obliquely and unevenly palmate, being divided into long slender lobes, a feature they share with the smaller upper leaves. In this species the leaves open when the flowers do, in early spring; they grow steadily larger until midsummer, but fall in the autumn. The flowers, shaped somewhat like Christmas roses, are very conspicuous despite their greenish colour. Soon after they open, the numerous golden yellow stamens fall away, leaving three prominent beaked carpels.

The main homeland of the green hellebore lies among the scrub and underwood of the mountainous districts of central Europe. It also grows wild in the south of England, though only in chalk and limestone woodlands. Often it is cultivated in gardens, on both sides of the Atlantic, for its decorative value.

2

Lesser Celandine

Ficaire *Ranunculus ficaria*

It seems odd that this very familar spring flower should have no true English name, but no doubt our forefathers regarded it as a buttercup. 'Celandine' is a herbalist's invention, as explained in the account of a similar but unrelated plant, the Greater Celandine, which appears in Plate 19. The French name of *ficaire* and the Latin specific name *ficarius* both signify 'fig-bearing', and arise from the plant's odd habit of bearing bulbils in the axis of its leaves — which structures were likened to fig fruits. These bulbils nearly always arise on plants growing in damp or overshaded spots, where they take the place of seeds in enabling the celandine to spread. In dry and open places normal flowers, with organs of both sexes, develop.

Every lover of the English countryside knows the celandine as one of the brightest and most regular harbingers of spring. Its golden blossoms gladden the eye in the dull days of March, or even February in the milder districts. It is one of the pre-vernal woodland plants, which expand both flower and leaf before the trees have donned their foliage. As summer advances it declines, storing its food within the cluster of fleshy tubers at its foot, until spring comes round again. Its usual haunt is broadleaved woodland, but it also grows along streamsides and hedgebanks; in gardens on clay soils it can — it must be confessed — become a bothersome weed.

The young leaves were formerly gathered and eaten as a salad or a cooked vegetable, largely because, being one of the first green leaves to appear, they were valued as a remedy for scurvy. Older leaves are too acid, as indeed are those of the related buttercups, to be palatable.

2
Hans Schwarzenbach 51.

PLATE 49

Mint Family *Labiatae*

Sticky Sage

Sauge glutineuse
Salvia glutinosa

Alpine Skullcap

Toque des Alpes
Scutellaria alpina

1

Sticky Sage

Sauge glutineuse — *Salvia glutinosa*

This is the largest of the European sages, growing up to three feet tall. It flourishes in shady places among the mountains, from Spain to Central Asia, but is not found wild in Britain. It often grows in dense masses in Switzerland, along the foothills, in gorges, and in clearings occasioned by the felling of beech and spruce. Every green part of this plant is enveloped by a dense fleece of sticky hairs — hence its name.

The apt size and form of the lipped yellow flowers enables one to see, quite easily, the arrangements for pollination. A pencil point pushed into the flower's open throat, will cause the two stamens to spring out from the upper 'helmet'. If an insect comes to gather nectar here, the pollen spills itself on to its back, to be carried away into another flower where it is lifted off by the forked stigma, which protrudes far out of the flower.

If you split the tube of the corolla, you will find within it, besides the two developed stamens, the rudiments of two others. These make up the characteristic number of four, which is found in most plants of the mint family or Labiatae, to which the sages belong. The garden sage, used as a seasoning, is the closely related *Salvia officinalis*.

2

Alpine Skullcap

Toque des Alpes — *Scutellaria alpina*

The English and French names of this quaint sage-like plant are derived from the cap-like shape of the upper half of the corolla, while the Latin name is based on the resemblance of that organ to a salver or flattened dish — *scutella.*

The form illustrated is the variety *lupulina,* which grows wild in Asia and is occasionally cultivated in American and British gardens. It exists in violet-blue, white, and parti-coloured strains, and is a hardy perennial with shoots that arise directly from the ground each spring. The flowers stand out bravely from a cluster of decorative pale green bracts.

The typical form of the species grows in southern Europe, including the south-west of Switzerland, as an alpine or sub-alpine plant. It ranks as a dwarf shrub, for it has both creeping and upright woody stems.

Our native common skullcap, *Scutellaria galericulata,* is a creeping perennial, with similar though less showy blue flowers, which is quite common along watersides and in damp pastures.

1
2
Hans Schwarzenbach 49

PLATE 50

Mint Family *Labiatae*

Scarlet Sage

Sauge écarlate
Salvia coccinea

Meadow Sage

Sauge des prés
Salvia pratensis

1

Scarlet Salvia

Sauge écarlate — *Salvia occinea*

This showy plant is a native of the southern United States of America, and has long been cultivated in Europe as a garden subject. It is really a perennial, but since it is very frost-tender it is usually grown in Britain as a half hardy annual. Seed is sown in a warm greenhouse in January and the plants bedded out in the border about June, to bloom until the first autumn frosts cut them down.

In this species, the flowers are remarkable in that not only the style, but also the two stamens, project far outside the helmet of the corolla. This arrangement is necessary because pollination is often achieved in a way that differs from that of most of the *Salvia* genus. The scarlet salvia is visited not only by insects, but also by humming birds. Because of their special mode of flight, these fascinating creatures are able to hover in front of the flower without actually perching. So poised, they thrust their long slender beaks into the throat of the corolla to sip the nectar. Since the stamens and style extend so far out, the bird brushes against them and thus assist in cross-pollination as it flits from flower to flower.

2

Meadow Sage

Salvia des prés — *Salvia pratensis*

This European species presents a classic and undeniable example of the adaptation that arises of a flower to an insect. Its flower has a long forked style that projects far out of the corolla, while hidden away below the helmet lie two stamens. When a honey bee or a bumble bee arrives, it forages with its snout for the nectaries that lie at the base of the corolla. In so doing it rubs against the stamens, which bend themselves down on to its back and drop their pollen there. Then the insect goes off to gather nectar from another flower, and the style of that one sweeps its back, so that the forked stigma picks up the load of fertilising pollen. To illustrate these reactions, you can substitute a pencil point for the insect's snout.

The meadow sage is rare in England, but it can sometimes be found in grassy places on the chalk and limestone hills of the southern counties. In the typical strain the showy flowers, borne in whorls, are deep purple, but in Europe both pink and white forms have been noted. The Latin name *Salvia* is connected with the verb *salveo*, to be well, because of the plant's healing properties.

1
2
2
Hans Schwarzenbach 49.

PLATE 51

Mint Family *Labiatae*

Clary

Sauge sclarée
Salvia sclarea

Monarda didyma

Melisse dorée
Monarda didyma

1

Clary

Sauge sclarée *Salvia sclarea*

This striking biennial plant is often grown in British and American gardens for its decorative effect. It is a native of the Mediterranean regions, extending as far north as Switzerland, where it is found wild in the cantons of Tessin and Valais. Its stems, leaves and flowers bear glands that secret a resin, which smells like a muscatel grape. If the fresh plant be steeped in ordinary wine, it will give it the flavour of a muscatel. This practice is now forbidden in the wine-growing lands, but nevertheless the Germans still call the plant the *Muscatelle*. The oil of Clary is used in perfumery, and a mucilage prepared from the seeds was once used to heal sore eyes and ulcers. The small pink flowers are hidden away in the axils of large conspicuous bracts, which form tufts at the tips of the stems. These bracts are smooth, oval to heart-shaped, and taper suddenly to a point. Their colour is whitish, strongly tinged with wine-red or mauve, with dark green veins and lower edges. This false 'inflorescence' is far more obvious than the true flowers, which are quite small and never grow out from among the shelter of the bracts. This peculiar plan is found in several other plants of the mint family, including other species of *Salvia* and marjoram. It is the bracts, rather than the petals, which attract the pollinating insects.

2

Monarda didyma

Melisse dorée *Monarda didyma*

This bright perennial, commonly grown in herbaceous borders, is a native of North America. It was introduced to Europe in the eighteenth century, and now and again it escapes from European gardens and tries to establish itself as a wild plant. At the very tip of its stem, and also quite often at a lower stage below, it produces whorls of numerous scarlet flowers, intermixed with scarlet bracts. The whole ensemble presents a striking tuft of floral colour.

Not only is this plant decorative, but it possess both real and imaginary medicinal properties. Like other members of the mint family, it has glandular hairs which secrete an odorous ethereal oil. Both the leaves and the flowers are therefore dried and used when required to infuse a herbal tea, which is taken to relieve digestive upsets, nervous troubles, bronchitis, and other ills. But the application of this herb to stem bleeding seems to rest on no better cause than the resemblance of its scarlet flowers to the colour of blood. The *Monarda* resembles the *Salvia* genus in having only two stamens, both of which are fertile.

2
Schwarzenbach 49

PLATE 52

Mint Family *Labiatae*

Water Mint

Menthe aquatique
Mentha aquatica

Bastard Balm

Mélitte à feuilles de mélisse
Melittis melisophyllum

1

Water Mint

Menthe aquatique *Mentha aquatica*

The mints have a well-known and distinctive smell which arises from the glandular hairs borne on the lower surfaces of their leaves and sepals. As wild plants, they live for the most part beside streams, among damp pastures, on peaty fens, and on water meadows subject to flooding, right across Europe and north-west Asia. Their flowers are borne in spherical clusters at the tips of the main stem and its branches. The corolla of each separate flower does not have the typical divided or lipped shape of the family Labiatae, but is almost regular. There are four petals and four stamens, but the sepals number five. In colour the flowers are usually lilac blue or mauve.
The water mint is very common along the fringes of slow-moving English rivers, particularly in our southern counties. It will grow as much as four feet tall, and often appears to be rooted below the water line. The common garden mint, a much smaller plant with more slender leaves, is properly the spear-mint, *Mentha spicata*; it is used to make sauce for roast lamb. On the North Downs of Surrey you may still find fields of the peppermint, *Mentha piperita*, which is grown to yield, by distillation, an essential oil; oil of peppermint is used to flavour sweetmeats, medicines, and toothpastes. Both these species are commonly cultivated as herbs in North America.

2

Bastard Balm

Mélitte à feuilles de mélisse *Melittis melisophyllum*

The odd names for this handsome plant, in English, French and Latin, record the fact that its leaves are very like those of the true balm, *Melissa officinalis*, a herb long cultivated in gardens for its healing properties when its oil is applied to wounds. No doubt the bastard balm was used for the same purpose, as it too contains a fragrant oil, scented like sweet woodruff.
In England the bastard balm, the largest-flowered wild plant of the order Labiatae, is something of a find for the botanist, who can only hope to encounter it in shady woods in Wales or the south-west. Its main home is in the warmer zones of central and southern Europe, where it is commonest amid scrub and open broadleaved woodland. It prefers lime-rich soil, and makes bold displays amid the Swiss Jura. Close relatives of the European species grow in North America and Japan, and it is believed to be an isolated relict plant from the Tertiary age. However, it has not lost its power of evolutionary variation, as is shown by the colour of its flowers, which range from pure white to deep pink.
Honey bees, bumble bees, and night-flying moths all visit the flower, and help in its pollination. They gather a rich booty, for there is ample nectar stored away high in the tube of the corolla. Children too know where this 'honey' lies, and will often pull off the flower to suck out its sweetness.

1
2
Hans Schwarzenbach 52

PLATE 53

Mint Family *Labiatae*

Geneva Bugle

Bugle de Genève
Ajuga genevensis

Ground Ivy

Lierre terrestre
Glechoma hederacea

Yellow Archangel

Ortie jaune
Galeobdolon luteum

Spotted Dead Nettle

Ortie morte
Lamium maculatum

1

Geneva Bugle

Bugle de Genève — *Ajuga genevensis*

The bugles differ from other plants of the order Labiatae in having only a very short upper lip, which indeed often appears to be absent. This handsome Swiss species grows on dry fields, rocky slopes and amid vineyards, where it blooms in May and June. Below each whorl of flowers there are conspicuous blue bracts. This species does not form runners.

The common bugle, which is native throughout Europe, including Britain, is a less showy plant which has a similar arrangement of blue flowers in whorls above each pair of leaves. It lacks coloured bracts, and spreads largely by means of runners. It is quite common in damp woods and hedge banks.

2

Ground Ivy

Lierre terrestre — *Glechoma hederacea*

All the names of this common European plant record its very superficial resemblance to the true ivy. It creeps along the floor of the woods and produces somewhat ivy-like leaves. Its flowers, however, are quite different; borne in whorls, they open in April and May and are lilac blue in colour. The whole plant is somewhat aromatic, and it was therefore used in herbal medicine as a tonic and cough cure.

3

Yellow Archangel

Ortie jaune — *Galeobdolon luteum*

The unusual name of this hedgerow plant suggests a fancied resemblance to a winged angel, arising from its open yellow petals, flecked with red, and its white anthers. It is also called the yellow dead nettle, or in French *ortie jaune,* because its foliage is like that of the stinging nettle, but harmless. One of the handsomest of common English wild flowers, it is much sought after by the bees.

4

Spotted Dead Nettle

Ortie morte — *Lamium maculatum*

Though common on the continent of Europe, this plant is scarce in Britain, and there is some doubt as to whether it is truly native. It differs from our common red dead-nettle in having larger flowers, while its leaves bear the peculiar pale spot that accounts for its name. Moreover, it is a perennial plant, whereas the red dead-nettle is annual. We also have a white-flowered perennial species. The resemblance of the leaves of these plants to those of the stinging nettle is believed to help protect them from grazing animals, and it certainly fools most people until the flowers appear. But more likely it is the result of chance parallel developments, among quite unrelated plants, resulting in similar forms.

4
3
2
1
Hans Schwarzenbach 44

Orchid Family *Orchidaceae*

Lizard Orchid

Orchis bouc
Himantoglossum hircinum

1

Lizard Orchid

Orchis bouc *Himantoglossum hircinum*

This orchid is one of the most exceptional European wild flowers, both for its extravagant blooms and its penetrating odour of billy-goats! A rarity in England, it is found only in the south, where it frequents the dry turf above chalk and limestone, or the sparse grass of the sand dunes. In Switzerland it is most common in the peculiar *garide* country of the Jura, where the arid soil over the limestone rocks, with their infrequent bushes, recall the *garigue* of the Mediterranean. Its range extends from Spain to Hungary. Green is the dominant colour of the flower. The helmet consists of three outer petals that are green without and purple within, with many purple spots, together with two much slighter inner petals. The very long lip petal below is greenish-yellow, changing to red along its edges; it has two shorter side branches, which are coloured in much the same way, but have peculiar wavy edges. The throat at the top of this lip petal is gorgeously spotted and streaked with reddish violet. Below the flower lies a short yellow spur which bears nectar. When the flower first opens, the lip lies rolled-up in a spiral; it soon elongates, and finally twists itself into a corkscrew-like shape.
The leaves wither away even while flowering is in progress. From time to time the plant fails to flower for one, or even for several years, and so people get the impression that it has vanished completely from some of its favourite haunts. But when it does bloom it is not readily overlooked, for it stands up to two feet tall above the turf.

Hans Schwarzenbach 51.

PLATE 55

Orchid Family | *Orchidaceae*

Soldier Orchid

Orchis militaire
Orchis militaris

Lady's Slipper

Sabot de Vénus
Cypripedium calceolus

1

Soldier Orchid

Orchis militaire — *Orchis militaris*

This splendid orchid grows a foot tall, and bears a glorious spike of pink blossom. It is, however, very rare in England, being known to survive only in two places among scrub on chalk, one haunt being in the Chilterns and the other in Suffolk. On the continent of Europe also it is getting scarce; it likes moist spots on lime-rich soils, but is disappearing before the spread of cultivation and the manuring of the fields.

The distinctive features of this orchid are these: its upper helmet is composed of three petals that run together and are rose-pink on their outer surface; the other upper petals are spread out, clear red in colour, and spotted with purple; the lip petal below is divided into three and bears a short spur. Below ground the soldier orchid has an undivided fleshy root.

2

Lady's Slipper

Sabot de Vénus — *Cypripedium calceolus*

This fairy-tale flower is sometimes called the Cinderella's slipper; and in France the 'shoe of Venus'. It has always been a rarity, and after the incautious botanists had published the names of its few English haunts it vanished so completely that it was long thought to be extinct. This impression was partly due to the fact that it does not bloom every year. It is now known to survive in only two woods, one in Yorkshire and one in Durham; both are on the limestone, but their exact situation is a closely-guarded secret.

On the mainland of Europe also this fine flower has been gathered to the verge of extermination. In many places it is protected by law, and people are being encouraged to enjoy it, and similar wild beauties, where they occur naturally rather than in a vase or a collector's cabinet. Allied species flourish in the North American woods.

The singular appearance of the flower arises from the lemon-yellow lip petal, which is curved over into the shape of a slipper. It is surrounded by other long slender petals of a dark purplish-brown hue. The lip petals offers an opening large enough for the entry of the insects that seek to feed on the nectar-bearing hairs on the inside of its recess. Entry is easy, but since the edges of the lip are curled over within, the insects are obliged to come out along a route very close to the stigma; this ensures pollination.

1
2
Hans Schwarzenbach 46.

PLATE 56

Rose Family *Rosaceae*

Norwegian Potentilla

Potentille de Norvège
Potentilla norvegica

Wild Strawberry

Fraisier des bois
Fragaria vesca

1

Norwegian Potentilla

Potentille de Norvège *Potentilla norvegica*

This plant and its close ally the sulphur potentilla, *P. recta*, are often grown in British and American rock gardens for their neat, gay, yellow blossoms. Here and there they take to the wilds, the sulphur potentilla preferring hot, dry waste ground, and this Norwegian potentilla the moister fields and stream sides.
You can recognise the Norwegian potentilla by the fact that its lower leaves are always divided into three leaflets, and look very like those of a strawberry. The upper stalk is much branched and bears smaller, simplified leaves. The yellow petals are always shorter than the green sepals, and the latter enlarge as the fruit ripens. The whole plant is distinctly hairy.

2

Wild Strawberry

Fraisier des bois *Fragaria vesca*

Although this wild plant was the original strawberry of cultivation, it has long been supplanted in the garden by the larger hybrid strawberry, *Fragaria ananassa*, which is a hybrid between the Chilean species, *F. chiloensis*, and the Virginian one, *F. virginiana*. The wild strawberry still flourishes in English woods, especially on dry chalky banks, and here and there one may come across local strains that have a delicious flavour never met with among the lush larger kinds. The name strawberry comes from the practice of strewing the beds in which the cultivated plants are grown, with straw, in order to protect the fruit, borne so close to the ground, from soiling and the attacks of slugs. The Welsh names for strawberries are *mefus* and *syfi*.
The wild strawberry, like the garden one, spreads over the ground by means of runners, which take root wherever they touch down. In this way it can insinuate itself among taller herbs and take advantage of any chance patch of light that reaches the woodland floor. As Shakespeare remarked, 'The strawberry groweth underneath the nettle.'
Early in June the strawberry opens small flowers on short upright stalks. Each flower has five green sepals, five white petals, many yellow stamens, and a group of carpels at its heart. After pollination by the bees, the petals and stamens fall away, the sepals enlarge and bend themselves back, while the centre of the flower, or receptacle, undergoes a strange but quite rapid transformation. It enlarges and bulges outwards to form a cone, bearing on its surface numerous maturing seeds. Under the warmth of the July sun it ripens, changing from green through white to bright red and finally crimson. Its flesh becomes sweet and deliciously flavoured, so that it soon tempts the birds, and the many animals, including mankind, who enjoy its soft flesh and inadvertently spread its tiny seeds. Among the French poets, the strawberry is aptly regarded as the symbol of seduction and sensuous pleasures.

Hans Schwarzenbach 49.

PLATE 57

Rose Family *Rosaceae*

Japanese Quince

Cognassier du Japon
Chaenomeles lagenaria

Japanese Quince

Cognassier du Japon *Chaenomeles lagenaria*

This beautiful Japanese shrub has been grown in Europe and America since 1815. It is sometimes planted as a single specimen, sometimes used to form ornamental hedges, but most frequently set below a wall to give its early blossom protection from spring gales. It bursts into bloom in March and early April, just as its fresh green leaves unfold, and the two together give the impression of a burning bush. The leaves become a rich glossy deep green, and persist on the bush well into the winter; indeed, in sheltered spots in mild districts this shrub is virtually evergreen.

In autumn the Japanese quince ripens its curious fruit, shaped like something between an apple and a pear, and with strong ridges towards its blunt tip. Green at first, it turns greenish yellow when fully ripe, and exceptionally fragrant; a single quince will perfume a whole room. Though not palatable when raw, it can be made into an excellent jam or jelly.

Many people know this shrub best by its former specific name of *japonica*. Actually there are two species, the pink-flowered one, shown here, being *Chaenomeles lagenaria*, while the fiery orange-red one, which bears yellow fruits, is now called C. *japonica*. Both are related to the common quince, *Cydonia vulgaris*, which is grown in old-fashioned gardens for its fragrant fruit, or raised by nurserymen as a stock for apples and pears.

Hans Schwarzenbach 50

PLATE 58

Rose Family *Rosaceae*

St Lucie Cherry

Faux-Merisier
Prunus mahaleb

Apple

Pommier
Malus sylvestris

1

St Lucie Cherry

Faux-Merisier *Prunus mahaleb*

This pretty cherry grows wild in warm and sunny places, especially on limestone rocks, all the way from Spain to Turkestan; it is particularly abundant on the Jura Mountains of France and Switzerland. Though not native in Britain or America, it is often grown as ornamental hedges, and even more frequently as a stock for cherries and morellos.

The St Lucie cherry may be a tree or a bush, and like other cherries it blooms late in the season. Its leaves are small, rounded, and pointed, with toothed edges and glistening upper surfaces. The white flowers form lax clusters. The fruits have a central stone, little flesh and a bitter taste. The wood is hard and heavy, and not easy to work. Nevertheless it is used to a large extent in turnery, because of its pleasant odour recalling new-mown hay, due to the presence of coumarin. The cherry-wood pipes, that look so ornamental because the bark is left in place, are made from the wood of this tree.

2

Apple

Pommier *Malus sylvestris*

To-day there at least 1,500 kinds of apple trees in cultivation, and several more in the wild; except for the peculiarities of their fruit they are all very much alike. Most are descended from the wild crab apple, *Malus sylvestris,* native to all Europe, including Britain, which bears smooth leaves ; or from another downy-leaved crab apple, *M. pumila,* which is native to south-east Europe but is often found in England as a wilding ; or from both these species.

Ever since Neolithic times, Europeans have cultivated apple trees wherever they have gone. The last of our fruit trees to flower, the apples provide the glorious high tide of spring blossom. Then, over the wide stretches of the orchards, one can enjoy the floral splendours of a sea of white enhanced by the pink and rose-red tints of the outer surfaces of the petals.

The apple is now our most valuable fruit tree, supporting great orchard industries in the warmer and sunnier regions of England and America. It uses are manifold — as dessert, in puddings and pies, sauces, jams and jellies, as fresh juice or fermented into cider (sweet or strong) — it is always good nourishment in one form or another.

1
2
Hans Schwarzenbach 53

PLATE 59

Figwort Family *Scrophulariaceae*

Great Mullein

Bouillon blanc
Verbascum thapsus

Snapdragon

Muflier
Antirrhinum majus

1

Great Mullein

Bouillon blanc *Verbascum thapsus*

During its first year of life this biennial plant forms nothing more than a rosette of large leaves down at ground level. But in its second year it extends a tall slender flower stalk to a height of four or even five feet, bearing a multitude of bright yellow flowers, each expanded into the shape of a wheel. The flower cluster as a whole has the form of a dense spike, but each bloom has in fact its own short stalk. Though the five petals of each bloom appear to be spread out flat, they are all united at their base into a short tube; they are unequal in size, those lower down being larger than those higher up. This irregularity is repeated in the stamens, the two lower ones being much longer than the three upper ones; the upper ones are clad in bristly hairs. These features show the relationship of the mullein to other plants of the figwort family, a group remarkable for their asymmetrical flowers.

The great mullein is quite a common wayside plant, and it is so handsome when in full bloom that it is sometimes spared a place in the garden. The whole plant is clad in dense whitish hairs. An old country name for it is Aaron's Rod, the speed of its growth having led to its association with that magical wand of the Bible.

2

Snapdragon

Muflier *Antirrhinum majus*

This plant has a striking appearance because of the form of its flowers, which give it its name. The word snapdragon arises from the way in which the two halves of its flower snap together like the jaws of a monster. It is also called 'calf's snout', and in French *muflier*, meaning snout-flower, or else *gueule-de-loup*, meaning wolf's muzzle. The upper portion of the flower consists of two petals that are bent back at the top; while three other reflexed petals make up the pouched lower lip; all five petals are united in the basal tube. If the flower be squeezed at the sides, its 'mouth' will open, but normally the lips are only forced apart by some nectar-seeking insect, such as a bumble bee.

The snapdragon is a native of the Mediterranean region, but has become thoroughly naturalised in Britain. It is commonest on the walls of ruined castle and abbeys, which suggests that monkish gardeners once brought it in and tended it. The many strains of snapdragons cultivated in British and American gardens show every possible combination of colour, especially white, bright yellow, and dark red. They are usually grown as annuals, though the wild plant is a perennial. Besides this common introduced species, there is also a smaller kind native to England; this is the lesser snapdagon, *Misopates orontium*, a pink-flowered biennial that grows on waste land.

1
2
1
H. Schwarzenbach 44

PLATE 60

Figwort Family *Scrophulariaceae*

Foxglove

Digitale pourpre
Digitalis purpurea

Yellow Foxglove

Digitale à grandes fleurs
Digitalis ambigua

1

Foxglove

Digitale pourpre *Digitalis purpurea*

One of the grandest of our woodland flowers is the foxglove, and it is not surprising that magnificent strains, taller and more flower-studded than the wild form, have been developed to grace gardens throughout Britain and America. It is a biennial, which during its first year forms only a low basal rosette of leaves; in the second year it shoots up, often to a height of five feet, a stout flowering stalk. This bears, in late summer, a brave display of drooping blossoms, each in the shape of the finger of a glove. Purplish red, with a mottling of reddish black spots, each is encircled with a patch of white; these spots lie within the tube, to serve as a guide to the nectar-seeking bees. The name 'foxglove' suggests that each flower might serve to hold a fox's paw; the Welsh name of *bysedd y cwn*, literally dog's finger, records a similar idea.

The foxglove is a western European plant, with a range along the Atlantic seaboard from Spain to Norway, but it does not extend far to the south-east, and is unknown as a wild plant in Switzerland. Rarely found far from the woods, it colonises hedgebanks and bushy thickets. It is most vigorous on fresh woodland clearings, to which the wind carries its multitudinous tiny seeds. In the absence of close competition, they spring up very freely, drawing on the materials released from the rich woodland soil, and in the following summer a sea of gorgeous foxglove blossom may result.

The foxglove contains two violent poisons, digitalin and digitoxin, which affect the heart. However, when used in carefully estimated quantities they control the heart's action, and hence play, even to-day, an important part in medicine. The active principles are extracted from the leaves of plants in their second season, before flowering; foxgloves are grown in Suffolk specially for this purpose, and their leaves are carefully harvested and dried.

2

Yellow Foxglove

Digitale à grandes fleurs *Digitalis ambigua*

The yellow foxglove, though nearly related to the common kind, flourishes best on the limestone rocks that the common sort dislikes. Its natural home lies towards the south and east of Europe, extending from France and Switzerland to the Ural Mountains. Gardeners on both sides of the Atlantic know it best as one of the parents of the beautiful modern hybrid foxgloves. The yellow foxglove is a plant of woods and rocky thickets. Its flowers are much less drooping than those of the common sort, and in fact often project horizontally.

Hans Schwarzenbach 48.

English Index

Latin Index